INDIANS

OSCEOLA, *Clark*
POCAHONTAS, *Seym...*
PONTIAC, *Peckham*
SACAGAWEA, *Seymour*
SEQUOYAH, *Snow*
SITTING BULL, *Stevens...*
SQUANTO, *Stevenson*
TECUMSEH, *Stevenson*

...RIGHT,

...E MAYO,

NAVAL HEROES

DAVID FARRAGUT, *Long*
GEORGE DEWEY, *Long*
JOHN PAUL JONES, *Snow*
MATTHEW CALBRAITH PERRY, *Scharbach*
OLIVER HAZARD PERRY, *Long*
RAPHAEL SEMMES, *Snow*
STEPHEN DECATUR, *Smith*

NOTED WIVES and MOTHERS

ABIGAIL ADAMS, *Wagoner*
DOLLY MADISON, *Monsell*
ELEANOR ROOSEVELT, *Weil*
JESSIE FREMONT, *Wagoner*
MARTHA WASHINGTON, *Wagoner*
MARY TODD LINCOLN, *Wilkie*
NANCY HANKS, *Stevenson*
RACHEL JACKSON, *Govan*

SCIENTISTS and INVENTORS

ABNER DOUBLEDAY, *Dunham*
ALBERT EINSTEIN, *Hammontree*
ALECK BELL, *Widdemer*
CYRUS MCCORMICK, *Dobler*
ELI WHITNEY, *Snow*
ELIAS HOWE, *Corcoran*
ELIZABETH BLACKWELL, *Henry*
GAIL BORDEN, *Paradis*
GEORGE CARVER, *Stevenson*
GEORGE EASTMAN, *Henry*
GEORGE PULLMAN, *Myers*
GEORGE WESTINGHOUSE, *Dunham*
HENRY FORD, *Aird and Ruddiman*
JOHN AUDUBON, *Mason*
JOHN BURROUGHS, *Fr...*
JOHN DEERE, *Bare*
LEE DEFOREST, *Dobler*
LUTHER BURBANK, *Br...*
MARIA MITCHELL, *Me...*
ROBERT FULTON, *Hen...*
SAMUEL MORSE, *Snow*
TOM EDISON, *Guthrid...*
WALTER REED, *Higgins*

LEADERS

BETSY ROSS, *Weil*
BOOKER T. WASHINGTON, *Stevenson*
CLARA BARTON, *Stevenson*
DAN BEARD, *Mason*
DOROTHEA DIX, *Melin*
FRANCES WILLARD, *Mason*
J. STERLING MORTON, *Moore*
JANE ADDAMS, *Wagoner*
JULIA WARD HOWE, *Wagoner*
JULIETTE LOW, *Higgins*
LILIUOKALANI, *Newman*
LUCRETIA MOTT, *Burnett*
MOLLY PITCHER, *Stevenson*
OLIVER WENDELL HOLMES, JR., *Dunham*
SUSAN ANTHONY, *Monsell*

SOLDIERS

ANTHONY WAYNE, *Stevenson*
BEDFORD FORREST, *Parks*
DAN MORGAN, *Bryant*
DOUGLAS MACARTHUR, *Long*
ETHAN ALLEN, *Winders*
FRANCIS MARION, *Steele*
GEORGE CUSTER, *Stevenson*
ISRAEL PUTNAM, *Stevenson*
JEB STUART, *Winders*
NATHANAEL GREENE, *Peckham*
ROBERT E. LEE, *Monsell*
SAM HOUSTON, *Stevenson*
TOM JACKSON, *Monsell*
U. S. GRANT, *Stevenson*
WILLIAM HENRY HARRISON, *Peckham*
ZACK TAYLOR, *Wilkie*

STATESMEN

ABE LINCOLN, *Stevenson*
ANDY JACKSON, *Stevenson*
DAN WEBSTER, *Smith*
...ROOSEVELT, *Weil*
..., *Monsell*
...OOVER, *Comfort*
...OE, *Widdemer*
...e Grummond and Delaune
...NNEDY, *Frisbee*
...ALL, *Monsell*
...EVELT, *Parks*
...WILSON, *Monsell*

John Smith

Jamestown Boy

Illustrated by Gray Morrow

John Smith

Jamestown Boy

By Thomas Frank Barton

THE **BOBBS-MERRILL** COMPANY, INC.
A SUBSIDIARY OF HOWARD W. SAMS & CO., INC.
Publishers • INDIANAPOLIS • NEW YORK

*To Tom, Jr., who inherited a fondness of stories
from his grandmother Sarah Smith (Barton) and
who as a child stimulated storytelling by
repeatedly saying, "Tell it again."*

Illustrations

Numerous smaller illustrations

Contents

Books by Thomas Frank Barton

JOHN SMITH: JAMESTOWN BOY
PATRICK HENRY: BOY SPOKESMAN

★ # John Smith

Jamestown Boy

Tending the Geese

"John! Oh, John!" called Mrs. Smith one beautiful afternoon in June, 1588. She was calling to her eight-year-old son John, who was sleeping under a lilac bush in the yard.

Mrs. Smith was sitting on a wooden bench in the shade of an apple tree, picking feathers from a live goose. She plucked one handful of feathers after another from the goose's body and stuffed them into a large coarse linen sack. Then she let the goose go.

After she released the goose, she called more loudly, "John! Wake up! Get ready to take the geese out to graze."

John rolled over on his back. He gazed lazily from under the lilac bush up into a beautiful clear sky. It felt good just to lie on the warm, soft earth.

Suddenly he hard a commotion that awakened him more than his mother's call. He jumped up and ran to his mother, who was holding to a stick hooked around the leg of a goose. Her face was flushed, her bonnet was flopping, and her hair was going this way and that.

Mrs. Smith had just caught Big Jack, the largest gander in the flock, and was having trouble holding him. He was floundering here and there, clawing the air and pounding the ground with his powerful wings.

Big Jack was the largest goose in the village of Willoughby, England. He had been the leader of Mrs. Smith's flock year after year, ever since she had started housekeeping. Now he was big and strong and strutted about as if he owned

12

the world. His feathers had been picked many times, but he never gave them up without a struggle.

John tried to help his mother handle the big gander. He watched for an opportunity to dart in without being struck by his powerful wings. Finally he grabbed the goose's neck with both hands and jumped astride his back.

At once Big Jack gasped for breath and stopped his violent struggle. John weighed only sixty pounds, but this was a heavy weight for a goose. Moreover, when John gripped the goose's neck he shut off much of the air that the goose needed for fighting.

John Smith was the son of a farmer named George Smith, who lived in the province of Lincolnshire on England's east coast, across the North Sea from the Netherlands. Mr. Smith grew crops and livestock and lived on land owned by Lord Willoughby.

Each person on the Smith farm had a particular job to do. Mr. Smith worked in the fields and looked after the farm animals. Mrs. Smith did the housework, including cleaning, baking bread, and making butter. John helped both his father and mother in every way he could.

Several times each year Mrs. Smith had to pluck feathers from the full-grown geese which the family raised. John helped to look after the geese by taking them to the pasture each day to secure food.

This was one of the picking seasons, and Mrs. Smith was catching the geese one after another to pluck their soft feathers. She had saved Big Jack until near the end because she knew that he would put up a fight.

"Thank goodness, you came to help me," she said. "Sometimes I think trying to pluck Big Jack's feathers isn't worth the struggle. Maybe we should just eat him."

"Oh, no!" pleaded John. "Big Jack doesn't mean any harm. Why, he's the largest and bravest gander in the village."

When Mrs. Smith didn't answer, John continued. "Big Jack is smart and everybody says he's the best guard in the village."

By now Big Jack was calm and John stood beside him stroking his back. The gander peeked out of one eye as if to say, "I'm ashamed of myself for fighting you."

Finally Mrs. Smith said, "John, I love Big Jack as much as you do. I've loved him ever since my father, your grandfather, gave him to me. At that time he was just an awkward, ugly gosling, but——"

John always felt a little uneasy when his mother stopped with the word "but." Somehow he felt that he should keep on talking to make sure the big goose was safe. "Now Big Jack is good for his feathers. Why, you'll get enough feathers from him to fill a whole bag. You can't do that from any of the other geese."

"All right, then," said Mrs. Smith with a smile. "We'll keep Big Jack if you'll make me a promise, John."

John nodded slowly. "What promise must I make?" he asked.

"You must promise to help me catch him each time I need to pluck his feathers," said his mother seriously.

"Of course I will," agreed John.

"Well, help me lead him over to the bench so I can start working on him," said Mrs. Smith. "You must take the flock to the field before dark."

John held Big Jack on the bench while Mrs. Smith plucked handful after handful of the gander's feathers and put them in a bag.

"I wish you would make me a pillow out of Big Jack's feathers," John said.

16

"For helping me, I'll be glad to make you a pillow," said Mrs. Smith.

That afternoon John and Big Jack walked side by side down the dirt lane, leading the flock of geese to the field. In one hand, John held a long looped rope, one end of which was fastened to a band around Big Jack's leg. The rope hung loose because Big Jack didn't need to be guided. He and John had walked down this lane to the field many times together.

Big Jack, strutting at the head of the flock of geese, held his head high. He was so tall that all the other geese could see him. From time to time, he checked to see whether the flock was following.

If a young goose or fuzzy gosling started to stray away from the flock or lagged behind to eat grass or to catch a bug, Big Jack called it back. And it obeyed.

John and Big Jack led the flock to a place

near a pond where the grass was long and green. The geese started to eat mouthful after mouthful of the green grass. They were very hungry because they had been penned up most of the day without food.

John drove a stick in the ground near the edge of the pond. Then he tied one end of the rope to the stick so that Big Jack could swim in the pond but could not cross it.

While the geese were busy feeding, John decided to do a little exploring along the edge of the pond. There always were interesting things to see along the boundary between the grass and water. Many reeds grew in the shallow water of the pond.

John parted the reeds and looked down at the shaded water. He saw a school of perch feeding among the reeds. He moved a little closer to see whether he could scoop up a perch with his hand.

18

Suddenly the geese started to honk and scurry about. Startled, John wondered what could be wrong and hurried to investigate. He could tell the geese were frightened.

When he reached the geese, he found some straggling out of the water and others staring at the pond. Frightened goslings were scurrying toward their mothers. Everywhere there was noise and confusion.

At once John noticed that the rope led to the pond and that Big Jack was out in the water. Apparently he was defending the flock from something in the water. Possibly something was attacking the young goslings.

Big Jack put his head in the water and pulled it out. He put it in again and, rocking backward, pulled a long, dark, wiggling object out of the water. Then he put his head in the water again, holding on to the object.

Time after time Big Jack rocked, pulling

19

the wiggling object out of the water and then putting it back. Each time he worked himself closer to the bank.

At last, when he reached shallow water, he gave a powerful twist with his body and neck and threw the object out of the pond onto the grass. John rushed over and tried to hit the object with a stick, but it managed to slither back toward the water.

Again Big Jack grabbed the object and threw it out of the pond and John swung at it with his stick. This time he hit it squarely, and it stopped wiggling. He looked at it closely. He and Big Jack had caught an eel.

At supper, John told his parents about Big Jack's scrap with the eel. They were as proud of John as John was of Big Jack.

"Now you won't need to worry about eating Big Jack," Mrs. Smith said. "Tomorrow we'll eat the eel you and Big Jack caught."

Playing in the Marshes

EARLY ONE morning John came sleepily to the kitchen and looked out the back door. The fresh air made him open his eyes wide.

"Good morning, John," said his mother. "You're up early today."

"Yes, I just couldn't sleep any longer, Mother," he replied.

Today he would take the geese to the pasture as usual, but he planned to take them during the morning. Then in the afternoon he hoped to play in the marshes.

John's mother hurried about the kitchen to prepare breakfast. Finally it was ready and the family sat down to eat. John felt very hungry after a good night's sleep.

While John and his parents ate, they talked about the day's work.

"I plan to work in the hayfield until dark," said Mr. Smith. "Can the two of you look after the chores this evening?"

"Yes, we'll milk the cows and feed the hogs," replied Mrs. Smith. "This morning I plan to churn. Then this afternoon I should like to pick the rest of the geese."

"I'll take the geese to the pasture this morning and bring them back at noon," John said. "I would like to play in the marshes this afternoon, but I'll come home early."

He ate hastily because he was eager to start. As he rose from the table, his mother urged him to have more bread and honey.

"No, thank you, Mother," he replied. "I must get the geese started to the pasture."

Soon John and Big Jack were proudly heading the geese down the lane toward the pasture. Coming behind them was John's father, driving a team of horses toward the hayfield.

The morning passed slowly. John kept waiting for the sun to reach the highest point in the sky. Then it would be noon and he could take the geese back to their pen.

At noon he shut the geese in the pen and did a few chores for his mother. He brought wood and a pail of water to the kitchen.

Mrs. Smith had prepared some pork pies for lunch, but John did not wait to eat. He was too eager to get started to the marsh. "I'll take a pie with me," he said.

He wrapped a pie in a cloth napkin and started for a stream that led to the marsh. After he reached the stream, he followed a footpath which mink had made walking along the stream. The path was lined with willows and alders.

At the edge of the marsh John came to a clump of willows where he thought he might find a woodcock nest. He must be careful where he stepped, however, lest he step on a soft spot in the ground and get stuck.

For safety he tied one end of a rope around a tree and the other end around his waist. Then if he happened to step on a soft spot, he could pull himself out. Slowly he worked his way into the marsh, looking for a woodcock nest. He wondered whether the nest would contain eggs or baby woodcocks.

Finding a nest was not easy, because woodcocks built their nests of dead sticks and leaves which were hard to see. The nests were almost the same color as the reeds and other plants growing in the marsh.

Finally, as John was making his way carefully through the undergrowth, he heard the fluttering of wings a short distance away. He looked and saw a woodcock tumbling about as if it had broken a wing.

"Where did you come from?" he asked. "And are you hurt or just pretending?"

He knew that certain birds and other animals pretend to be hurt in order to protect their young. By pretending, they manage to lead people away from their nest.

John wasn't tricked. He looked carefully around a clump of willows and found a shallow nest containing two baby birds. He didn't disturb the birds, because he didn't want their parents to abandon them.

By and by he sat down to eat his pork pie. As he loosened the cloth napkin, he found dozens of ants trying to reach the food. He shook them off and started to eat.

As he ate, he watched life go on around him in the marsh. Mrs. Woodcock returned to her nest to check on the baby birds. Then she flew away as if going to tell Mr. Woodcock that the babies were safe.

A crane settled in a near-by stream and started to pick its food out of the water. Dozens of birds fluttered about, some singing gaily, some selecting materials for nests, and others carrying food to their young. Swarms of insects buzzed through the air.

After John finished eating, he leaned back to rest and fell asleep. Soon he was awakened by a great noise all about him. Dozens of birds were flying about, crying in alarm.

The trouble seemed to be in a willow tree near by. John picked up a stick and started toward the tree. Then he saw a big snake on a dead limb, pulling its head out of a hole in the tree. In its mouth it held a baby bird which it swallowed immediately.

Again it put its head in the hole and brought out a baby bird. As he watched the snake, John noticed that its body contained six bulges. It must have eaten six of the baby birds already, he decided.

He remembered the two baby woodcock in the nest near by and wondered whether or not they were safe. He hurried to the nest and found that they were gone. Evidently the snake had eaten them, too.

John was angry and picked up a big stick. He struck the snake several blows until he was certain it was dead. "Now you won't eat any more baby birds," he said.

By now it was late afternoon and John started for home. He had scarcely started, however, when he saw a clump of marsh grass in front of him wave as if something were hiding in it.

"I wonder why that grass is waving?" he thought. "Could a wild animal of some sort be wandering about in the marsh?" He hesitated a moment, wondering what to do. Then he picked up another stick and holding it in striking position moved forward cautiously.

When he reached the grass he stopped suddenly and laughed with surprise and relief. There, struggling and half-buried in the mud, was a pig. It had evidently strayed too far from the path and become stuck in the mire. By now it was too exhausted even to squeal.

"What should I do?" thought John. "Shall I try to get the pig out or shall I go for help? If I go for help, the pig will die before I can get back. I must do what I can do by myself."

Carefully he slipped his rope around the pig's two front legs and made a slip knot so that he could pull the rope tight. He put some branches in the mud under the pig to keep it from sinking more. Then, bracing himself against a willow, he started to pull on the rope.

Fortunately he was able to bring the pig out a few inches. He pulled again and once more

was able to lift the pig a few inches. By now the pig began to help itself with its rear feet. Soon it was on solid ground.

John untied the rope from the pig's front feet

and the pig, still exhausted, started to walk slowly toward Willoughby. It belonged to Mr. Mumby in the village and was eager to return home. When the pig reached the Mumby home, it turned in the yard.

"I had missed the pig," Mr. Mumby told John, "and wondered what had become of it. Where did you find it? It's covered with mud."

"It was in the marsh," said John. He told how he had pulled the pig out of the mud.

"I'm grateful to you, John," Mr. Mumby said. "I wouldn't want to lose that pig. Will you stay and have supper with us?"

"Thank you, but I must hurry home," John said. "I promised to help with the chores."

"Then take a loaf of fresh bread with you," said Mrs. Mumby. "You're a good boy."

That night John was very happy as he helped his mother with the chores. He felt good to know that he had rescued the pig.

The Annual Sheep Shearing

"HELLO! Is anybody home?" The voice calling was a man's and came from outside.

Mrs. Smith, who was kneading bread dough in the kitchen, lifted her head. "Who is that calling?" she asked. "John, look out and tell me who is out there."

John went to the door and saw a man on horseback in front of the cottage. "I don't know him, but he works for Lord Willoughby," he said. "I've seen him riding along the lane that leads to Lord Willoughby's house."

The man called again. "I have a message from Lord Willoughby for George Smith."

"Go out and take the message for your father," said Mrs. Smith.

John went outside. "My father isn't here, but I'll take the message," he said.

The rider looked down at John. "Lord Willoughby plans to hold a sheep shearing at Beech Grove one week from today," he said. "He wants your father to come. Will you be sure to give him the message?"

"Yes, sir," replied John.

"You look like a healthy lad," the man went on. "You may come along with your father if you wish. We'll find work for you."

John stood watching as the man rode away. He could scarcely believe that he had been invited to a shearing. What work could he possibly do at a shearing?

"What did the man want?" called Mrs. Smith from the house.

"He wanted to tell Father that Lord Willoughby plans to hold a shearing at Beech Grove one week from today. He said for Father to come, and he invited me, too."

"You?" asked Mrs. Smith, bewildered. "What can you do at a sheep shearing?"

"I don't know, but I'd like to go."

At the supper table that night Mrs. Smith said to her husband, "Lord Willoughby's messenger came today. Guess what he wants?"

"I expect he wants me to come help shear sheep," replied Mr. Smith. "It's shearing time."

"He not only wants you to come, but he invited John, too," Mrs. Smith added. "I'm surprised that he would ask a nine-year-old boy to help? What can John do?"

"Don't get excited," Mr. Smith said. "John can help herd the sheep. Then one of the herders can help with the shearing."

"Well, I still think John is too young to go," said Mrs. Smith.

34

The week before the shearing passed very slowly for John. Each day he became more excited. This would be his first time to work and eat and sleep away from home.

Finally the day arrived. Early in the morning Mr. Smith and John walked to Beech Grove, two miles away. When they arrived they found men and boys coming from all directions. John was the youngest boy there.

The sheep, many of them ewes with lambs, had been brought from the pastures, so they could be caught for shearing. John's job was to help other boys watch the sheep and keep them from wandering away. He had never seen so many sheep before in his life.

Soon the shearing got under way. Each man caught a ewe from the flock and started to clip off the wool with big shears. Later the wool or fleece would be cleaned and made into yarn, then used for making cloth.

The men and boys ate food cooked over camp-fires and slept on sheepskins at night. Each evening they sat around the campfires and told stories and sang songs. John liked the soft sheep-skin on which he slept and wished he could have one like it to take home.

As the days passed, John found the camp less and less exciting. He discovered that shearing sheep was hard, smelly work. The air was filled with the unpleasant odors of sweat from the men and oil from the wool.

One morning the men found a ewe with a broken leg. The camp workers killed the ewe and hung her skin in a tree to dry. This was the very kind of skin John wanted.

Later in the morning Lord Willoughby rode into camp on a beautiful white horse. He noticed the sheepskin hanging in the tree and asked about it. When he heard about the ewe, he shook his head sadly and said, "We'll dispose of the sheepskin later, perhaps as a reward to someone. I'll be back to look after it."

On the last day of the shearing John was stationed along a stream a short distance from the camp. His job was to watch for straying sheep that might try to follow the stream into a thick woods. Only a few sheep were left to be shorn by this time.

Around noon John heard frantic bleating and noticed a stampeding flock running toward the forest. The flock was led by Lord Willoughby's favorite ram. The ram held his horns high in the air and ran several yards ahead of the flock, leaping from rock to rock in the stream.

John wondered what to do, but there was little time to think. He grabbed his herding stick and rushed out to try to stop the ram. The ram kept coming and in desperation John struck the animal on the head.

The ram, partly stunned and maddened,

wheeled and rushed directly toward John. Just as the ram reached him, John seized one of his horns and leaped on his back. Startled, the ram whirled and ran toward the camp.

Suddenly leaderless, the rest of the sheep stopped running and started to turn back. A herder who had rushed up to help John shouted, "Hold on, John! Hold on!"

The ram raced toward camp with John clinging desperately to his thick wool. As the ram sped past the wool from the day's shearing, which had been gathered in a pile in the center of the camp, John suddenly let go and threw himself toward the pile.

The wool cushioned his fall, but he was slightly stunned and lay motionless for a moment or two. Then he heard people running and opened his eyes to see Lord Willoughby and several of the shearers gathered around him. As he saw Lord Willoughby, John's heart sank.

What would the latter think about John's riding his prize ram? What would he do?

"John Smith," said Lord Willoughby, "you are our youngest worker, but you have turned out to be a hero. If you had not stopped the sheep they would now be lost in the woods."

"Thank you, sir," replied John. "I only did what I could."

"Well, you saved us all kinds of trouble," Lord Willoughby continued. "In return for your bravery, let me give you the sheepskin that we were saving for a reward."

One of the shearers brought the sheepskin to John. "I've wanted a sheepskin to sleep on for a long time," John said happily. "Now I really have one."

That night John and his father returned home. John's mother was surprised when he told her what had happened. "I'm very proud of you," she said. "You have come back a hero."

Where Does the Sea Go?

"John! John! Wake up!" called his mother, shaking him gently.

John opened and closed his eyes. "I'm awake," he said and turned on his back.

"Well, it's time to get up if you are going to the seashore with your father," said his mother. "He is eager to get started."

Today Mr. Smith was to drive to a fishing village several miles away to get a cartload of fresh fish for Lord Willoughby. He had promised to take John, who always enjoyed going to the seashore with his father.

The family sat down at the table and ate a hurried breakfast, which Mrs. Smith had cooked in the fireplace. The air outside was slightly raw and the heat from the fireplace felt pleasant. "I'm afraid you'll have a chilly ride this morning," Mrs. Smith said.

"We'll manage to keep warm," said Mr. Smith. "If we get cold, we can climb down from the cart and walk."

After breakfast Mr. Smith brought his favorite horse, Dobbin, from the stable and hitched him to a two-wheeled cart. Then he and John climbed into the cart and started off. A thick fog hung over the land and they could see only a short distance ahead.

They started down the road, which was little more than a lane. Soon they came to the marshland, where the fog was thicker than before. Finally the fog became so thick that they could scarcely see.

"Isn't it dangerous to travel through the

42

marshes in a fog like this, Father?" John asked a little anxiously.

"Yes, we might lose our way," replied Mr. Smith. "There's some danger of being held up by robbers, too, I suppose. It's easy for robbers to hide in a fog like this."

"If we might be robbed shouldn't we turn back and go after the fish some other day?" asked John. "Do we have to go now?"

"Yes, Lord Willoughby expects us to get the fish today," said Mr. Smith. "He is having a banquet at his house tonight."

The farther Mr. Smith and John went into the marshland, the thicker the fog seemed to become. Mr. Smith had to keep talking to Dobbin to encourage him to keep going.

Several times Dobbin stopped or jumped to one side and John was afraid robbers were lurking near by. Each time Mr. Smith jumped down from the cart and ran to pat Dobbin to reassure him. Sometimes he led Dobbin or walked along beside him for a while.

After an hour or so, the fog began to disappear. Soon the sun began to shine and the fog disappeared completely. Then everything in the marsh seemed to come alive.

By and by Mr. Smith decided to stop for a while to let Dobbin rest. He halted beside a pond where Dobbin could get a drink and where he and John could sit on the bank and talk.

Before long they noticed a flock of wild ducks swimming and feeding at the edge of the pond. The flock included large mother ducks, small ducklings, and a drake. The ducklings were having great fun in the water.

Suddenly the large ducks began to quack and flutter about. The mother ducks moved to form a ring around the little ducklings as if to protect them. Then the drake started to lead the flock out into the pond.

Soon John and his father discovered why the ducks were excited. A big pike had caught one of the ducklings by the leg and it was struggling to get away. The pike had the duckling's leg clamped firmly in its mouth.

John wished he could help the duckling somehow. He wished the leg would break off so that the duckling could get away. He had seen many one-legged ducks.

Soon the pike pulled the duckling under water. It knew that it could breathe underwater and the duckling could not. This seemed to be the end for the duckling.

Shortly the pike brought the duckling to the surface of the water again. The duckling was too near dead to flap its wings or to quack. Suddenly the big pike gave a lunge and the poor duckling disappeared completely.

"That was a terrible sight," said John. "I hate to see things like that happen."

"Yes, I know," replied Mr. Smith, "but here in the marshland many animals feed on other animals. Certain fish not only eat ducklings, but they eat frogs and other fish. Certain birds eat frogs and fish and other small animals. The marshes are full of animal hunters, waiting to prey on one another."

At last John and his father climbed into the cart and started on. They hoped to reach the village by the middle of the morning. They could spend only a couple of hours there, however, because they had to deliver Lord Willoughby's fish by the middle of the afternoon.

"I'm eager to get there," said John, "and look out on the water. It makes me want to get on a ship and go exploring."

"There's a great mystery about the sea," said Mr. Smith, patting John's shoulder.

Before long they began to approach the fishing village. The air seemed to smell fresher and different kinds of birds were flying about. Even the plant life along the way seemed to be different, John thought.

Mr. Smith explained that sea water was salty and that some of it seeped into the land near the sea. This salty water helped to explain why the animals and plants were different.

When Mr. Smith and John reached the village, John jumped excitedly from the cart. He ran to the shore and stood looking silently out over the water. He watched the waves that came rolling in to break into foam on the near-by beach, and he listened to their wavering roar.

The fishing boats had just returned with their morning catch. Barefooted men and boys splashed through the water, carrying baskets of fish from the boats to the shore. At the water's edge several people were waiting with tubs to purchase fish. Mr. Smith purchased three tubs of fish and placed them in his cart. He packed wet barley straw around the fish to help keep them cool. He wanted the fish to be fresh for Lord Willoughby's banquet.

In the meantime, John took off his shoes and started to help carry fish from the boats. He talked with the boys and asked them many questions about the sea and about fishing. He climbed into one of the fishing boats after it was empty to see what it was like.

The fishermen and boys liked John and did their best to tell him what he wanted to know. Some of them invited him to their homes to eat a meal of fried fish, but Mr. Smith said there wouldn't be time. They would have to leave soon in order to get the fish to Lord Willoughby's house in time for the banquet.

"How would you like to stay here and go fishing with us tomorrow?" asked one of the fishermen. "Then your father could come to get you in two or three days."

"No, thank you," replied John, "but I would like to come back soon. Then maybe I will stay and go fishing with you."

"Well, I think you would make a good sailor," said the man. "I can tell by looking at you. Would you like to be a sailor?"

John's eyes lighted with eagerness. "Yes, more than anything else," he said.

"There is no chance for John to be a sailor," said Mr. Smith. "He is my oldest son and will have to take over the farm when I die or become too old to work, just as I did when my father died. John will be a farmer."

John was disturbed by his father's remark. Somehow he could feel the sea drawing him. "Where does the sea go?" he asked. "What would I find out there?"

"Just more water," answered his father, climbing into the cart. "We haven't time to stay here any longer."

"Your father is right," said the fisherman. "The water goes on and on. Beyond it lie many strange countries and people."

"Someday I'd like to see those countries," John said as he climbed into the cart.

"I hope you have a safe trip with the fish," called the fisherman, "and I hope you'll come again soon."

As the cart pulled away, John looked back longingly. "Someday I'll sail out to see where the sea goes," he promised himself.

After his visit to the fishing village, the trip home seemed boring to John. He wasn't even interested in watching things in the marsh that he usually enjoyed. Somehow he couldn't get the sea out of his mind.

At last Mr. Smith pulled up at Lord Willoughby's manor house. Lord Willoughby came out to thank Mr. Smith while the servants carried the fish into the house. "I can always

depend on you, George," he said. "I hope your son here will grow up to be as dependable as you are."

"I've just been telling him that he must take over my farm someday," said Mr. Smith. "Our family has held land from you and your family for a long time."

"Yes, I know," John said. "But after today I want to be a sailor."

Two Frightened Boys

ONE MORNING John went to Lord Willoughby's house to meet his friend Robert, Lord Willoughby's oldest son. Both boys were ten years old and had become close friends. Today they planned to go fishing together.

The boys had fun together even though their families were of different rank. John's father was just a tenant farmer living on Lord Willoughby's land. Someday Robert, as Lord Willoughby's oldest son, would inherit all his land. Then John, the oldest son of George Smith, would be a tenant on Robert's land.

John was usually the leader when the two

boys played together. He knew more about the surroundings, such as the marshland, woods, and wildlife, because Robert seldom was allowed to play away from home.

Today would be a special day for Robert. He and John were going fishing.

"Are you ready?" John called when he came to the manor house.

The two boys went to a stream that led into a forest. They threw their lines in the water and waited for the fish to bite. First one boy caught a fish and then the other.

Finally the boys began to tire of fishing and decided to do something else. "Let's go into the forest and play 'I spy,'" said John. "There are many things to see in the forest."

Robert had never been in the forest before and was eager to see what it was like. "All right," he said, "but you're better about seeing things than I am."

The boys had scarcely entered the forest when John called out, "I spy!"

"What do you see?" asked Robert. "I don't see anything unusual."

"Look directly above your head at the limb of that tree," said John. "If it were a snake, it could drop on you, but it isn't a snake."

Robert looked and saw something that looked round like a ball encircling a large limb of the tree. He could see that it looked fuzzy and was almost a foot across.

"What is it?" he asked.

"It's a swarm of wild honey bees," John answered. "Hundreds of bees."

"Bees? I thought bees lived in hollow trees," Robert said.

"They do," said John, "but this is a new swarm out looking for a home. When a new queen appears in a colony of bees the old queen leaves with part of the swarm to find a new home and start a new colony. These bees must have left the old colony just a short while ago."

"Is there a queen in this swarm of bees?" Robert asked excitedly.

"Yes," said John. "The queen is the leader of the swarm, but she has many helpers."

"I wish we could see the queen," Robert said. "Is there any way to see her?"

"No," John replied. "We musn't disturb the swarm. If we were to hit it with a stick hundreds of bees would swoop down on us. They might even sting us to death."

"Then let's get out of here before they notice us!" Robert exclaimed.

"There must be another colony of bees near by," John said thoughtfully. "Let's look for a colony that's already living in a hollow tree."

"How can we find one?" asked Robert. "Where shall we look?"

"Bees gather nectar from flowers to make

honey," explained John. "First we look for a patch of flowers. Then if bees are gathering nectar from the flowers, we'll follow them. They'll go straight to their colony."

"But we can't run as fast as bees can fly," said Robert.

"No, but we can follow a string of bees all going to the same colony," said John. "If we lose sight of one bee we can watch for another. In this way we'll find their colony."

The boys found some bees buzzing over a patch of flowers and started to follow them. They soon lost the first bees but noticed that others were flying in the same direction. In this way they kept following bees for about a quarter of a mile.

At last the boys came to a big beech tree with a big hole in one side. Bees were buzzing in and out of the hole. This was the home of the colony of bees.

Robert stood looking up at the bees, hoping to see the queen. In the meantime John noticed that the trunk of the tree was hollow near the bottom and crawled inside. When Robert looked around for John, he had disappeared.

At first Robert was frightened. How could John have disappeared so rapidly? Where had he gone? Surely he hadn't started for home.

Robert scarcely knew what to do. He felt deserted. Finally he called, "John! Oh, John! Where are you?"

"I'm here," came a muffled answer.

Robert looked in the direction of the sound but couldn't see John. He was only a few feet away from the tree, but John was hidden inside the hollow trunk.

"Where are you?" Robert called again. "Tell me where to look."

Just then John crawled out of the hollow tree and began to laugh. "I found a good place to

hide," he said. "It's almost like a little room in the tree. We both could hide in there if we wanted to."

"Let's both crawl in," said Robert. "I want to see what it's like inside."

The two boys crawled into the hole. Once they were inside they felt as if they were hidden from the rest of the world.

"We have a good place to hide but no reason for hiding," John said.

Just then the boys heard a noise outside the tree. Two men were talking. Then came the sound of the heavy steps of a horse and cracking of dry sticks.

John peered out to see what was happening. "What do you see?" Robert whispered.

"Two mean-looking men with long beards," John answered. "One of them has a red beard and an ugly scar on his face. The other one has a black beard and a crooked nose. They're lead-

60

ing a horse hitched to a sledge and the sledge is loaded with something covered with canvas."

"Are they robbers?" asked Robert, trembling with fear.

"I don't think so," John replied. "We'll have to wait to find out."

Just then the man leading the horse stopped and examined the sledge closely. It was made of thick boards with two saplings for runners, curved like the runners of a sled.

"We'd better stop here and fix the sledge," he said. "One of the saplings broke when we hit a rock a while ago and it won't last until we reach the coast. That cannon is heavy and the sledge runners will soon wear out."

"What did he say?" whispered Robert.

"Sh!" John said. "The men are smugglers. They have stolen a cannon and are dragging it to the coast to sell."

The second man bent to study the sledge runner, then nodded in agreement. "Yes, we'll have to replace that runner," he said. "It's broken clean through."

"Well, one thing's certain," said the other. "That cannon is too heavy to carry."

"First let's find a good curved sapling and replace the runner," his companion went on. "Then we'll catch some fish and cook a good meal. I'm hungry. We can start for the coast again in the morning."

When the boys heard this suggestion they became frightened. "We may have to hide here all night," Robert whispered. "What will our parents think? They will come looking for us and maybe the smugglers will kill them."

"Don't get excited," John answered calmly. "We'll just hide until the men go fishing, then we'll crawl out and go home."

The two smugglers started to unhitch the horse. Suddenly one of them looked up and saw the bees flying in and out of the tree. "Look, mate!" he cried. "This is a bee tree!"

"You're right," said the other. "Let's get away from here. Those bees could cause all kinds of trouble."

The men quickly led the horse away. Soon the boys could hear them chopping down a tree some distance away.

"We're lucky," said John. "Now we can crawl out and start for home."

The boys ran as fast as their legs could carry them. They never stopped until they reached the edge of the forest. Then they dropped down in some tall grass to rest.

"I'm still frightened," said Robert.

"So am I," John answered. "This certainly has been an exciting day."

Soon the boys hurried on. As John left Robert he called, "Don't forget to tell your parents about the bee tree."

Another Day
of Fun

ONE BEAUTIFUL August day in 1590 John and
Robert decided to play soldier. Each boy carried a pair of stilts which he planned to use
while walking in the marsh.

Robert was interested in wars because his
father had been a soldier in Europe. He often
asked his father to tell about some of the battles
in which he had fought.

The boys thought that if they were ever
needed to fight a war in marshy land like that
around home, it would be helpful to know how
to walk on stilts. Today they were going to
practice walking on stilts in the marsh.

64

"Do you really think we can walk in the marsh on these stilts?" asked Robert.

"Yes, with a little practice," said John, "but we must be careful."

"Careful of what?"

"Of bogs chiefly," said John. "Bogs can be tricky sometimes."

"Bogs?" Robert looked puzzled.

"Don't you know what bogs are?"

"I've heard of them," Robert said, "but I don't know exactly what they are."

"Well, a bog is a deep pond in a marsh, covered with vines and weeds and decayed vegetation. The vegetation covers the pond completely and you can't see the water beneath it. If you step on the vegetation, though, you can feel it move under your feet."

"Ugh! It doesn't sound very pleasant," Robert said. "What happens if you break through the vegetation?"

"You're likely to drown in the water beneath," answered John. "Many men and animals have drowned in bogs."

"If they fall in, can't they come back up through the same holes?" asked Robert.

"No, the vegetation usually closes in over the holes and they are caught in the water," said John. "They have no way to escape."

The boys continued to walk along the edge of the marsh, looking for a suitable place to try out their stilts. Soon they came to a pond from which there came a terrible stench. The decaying bodies of several dead animals floated in the water.

The boys hurried on, hoping to get away from the signs of death and the terrible odor. Soon they came to another pond.

"I hope this pond is a better place to play than the other one," said Robert.

As soon as they reached the pond, however,

John pointed to the carcasses of three dead sheep. The tendons on their back legs had been cut so that they couldn't walk. Animals whose tendons have been cut in this way are said to be hamstrung.

"Look," John said. "Those poor sheep have been hamstrung and left here to die. They must have died horrible deaths."

"Who would do something as mean as that to the sheep?" asked Robert.

"There are some mighty mean men in the world," replied John. "Robbers must have caught these sheep. They didn't want the sheep to escape, so they cut their tendons to keep them from walking."

"Why didn't they take the sheep with them?" asked Robert.

"Any one of several things may have happened," John replied. "Evidently they expected to come back after the sheep and never came.

Maybe they couldn't come back with a horse or boat, or maybe they became lost and couldn't find their way back. Anyhow, they left the sheep here to starve to death."

The boys walked on until they came to a pond which seemed to be fairly clean.

"This looks like a good place to try our stilts," John said. "I'll go first." He started to take off his clothes. "I'll leave my clothes here on the bank so they won't get wet."

"Do you think you'll fall?" asked Robert.

"I'll probably fall several times," John said. "It will take practice to learn how to walk on stilts in water."

He tied one end of a rope around his waist and handed the other end to Robert. "Now if I fall in the water or start to sink through the vegetation, you can pull me out."

"I hope nothing happens," Robert said.

"So do I," said John.

John got on his stilts and started to walk boldly into the water. He took a dozen steps and seemed to be doing fine. Suddenly one of his stilts stuck in the bottom of the pond and he pitched headfirst into the water.

At once Robert braced himself and started to pull on the rope, but before he could take the slack out of it John was standing on his feet. He wiped the water from his eyes and reached for his stilts. "Well, that's my first fall," he said with a laugh.

Getting back on the stilts, he started and fell once more. Again and again he started and fell. Finally he learned to balance himself and was able to walk wherever he wished in the pond without difficulty. At last he came back to the bank where Robert was waiting.

"Now it's your turn, Robert," he said.

Robert took off his clothes and tied the rope around his waist as John had done. "Well, here

I go," he said. He had hardly started before he fell with a loud splash.

Only his pride was hurt, and he got up and started again. This time he went all around the pond without falling.

"Good for you!" John said. "You've learned to walk better than I. I am proud of you."

Now both boys got on their stilts and walked around the pond. They learned to balance themselves even if their stilts got stuck in the mud. No longer did they fall.

"You know, soldiers often need to send messages," John said. "We should learn how to send secret messages to each other."

"How can we do that here?" asked Robert. "We can't write letters and we can't talk because everyone would hear us."

"That's true, but we can make up a code of some kind—make sounds that mean things to us and to nobody else."

"What do you mean?"

"We could croak like a frog, for example," John went on. "One croak could mean, 'Come here.' Two croaks could mean, 'Answer to let me know where you are.' Three croaks could mean, 'Run.' Four croaks could mean, 'Hide.' Five croaks could mean, 'Go to the fort.' "

"Those would be easy to remember," Robert said, "but how would I answer you?"

John thought a moment, then said, "You could caw like a crow. You could caw once to say, 'I'm coming,' twice to say, 'Here I am,' three times to say, 'I understand,' and four times to say, 'I'm going to the fort.' "

Robert grew enthusiastic. "We could send all kinds of messages with a code like that, and nobody could understand us or even know we were sending messages."

"Yes, and if we needed them we could make up other messages, too," John said. "Let's see how the code works."

The two boys parted so that neither could see the other. Then John croaked twice. Immediately Robert cawed twice to let John know where he was hiding. Next John croaked once and Robert came running from the tall clump of grass where he had been hiding. "It works! It works!" he cried excitedly.

"Yes," John said, delighted himself. "We've learned two things today. We've learned how to walk on stilts and we've learned how to send secret messages."

"Those are important things to know, too," Robert said seriously as the boys picked up their stilts and started home.

John nodded. "Yes, I think we're ready for almost any enemy we might find here in the marsh," he said.

Bird Poachers on Thieves' Island

"Run!" John shouted. "Faster! Faster!"

Robert increased his speed. He thrust one end of his long vaulting pole into the mud of the small stream and threw himself up and out over the water.

"Yow-w-w!" He hit the water with a resounding splash and disappeared. He was on his feet again in a moment, waist-deep in water, spluttering and wiping the water from his eyes. "I did it again!" he said disgustedly.

He rescued the pole before it floated away and waded ashore, where John was watching.

The two boys had cut long poles and were

learning how to vault over small streams and other stretches of water. John could run up to a stream and vault across readily, but Robert was having trouble.

"Well, I've been practicing longer than you have," John said. "I just run up to the stream as if I'm going to run right into the water. Then I put my pole down quickly and sort of lift myself across."

"I think I must slow up before I reach the water," Robert said. "Anyhow, I don't get all the way across."

The two boys were on their way to an abandoned pit which they used for a fort. At one time men had taken peat from the pit and had left a big hole at the base of a hill. The hole was much like a cave, with its entrance concealed by a large bush that had grown up in front of it. Few people knew the pit was there.

The boys kept many things in their fort, most-

ly things for carrying on make-believe war.
They had darts, bows and arrows, and stones
to throw at make-believe enemies. They kept
their stilts there so they would not have to carry
them back and forth from home.

Today when the boys reached their fort they
sat down on some sheepskins to talk. "What
shall we do?" asked Robert.

"Let's go to Thieves' Island," John suggested.
"Maybe we'll see something exciting."

Thieves' Island was a small island in the
center of a large, shallow pond in the marsh.
Thieves were supposed to hide there until they
could make plans to escape with their stolen
goods. Several thieves had been killed on the
island, the boys had heard.

There was only one way to reach the island
by land. A narrow ridge of land extended across
the water to the island. It was too narrow for a
road, but people could walk across it if they

were careful. The ridge was covered with tall grass and shrubs.

The boys started to work their way along the ridge. The ground was wet and slippery and several times they almost slid into the water, but they managed to save themselves. Finally they came to the island.

"What shall we do now?" asked Robert.

"Let's look around," said John, "but we must be careful. If there are any thieves here, we don't want them to see us or hear us. We'd better separate. You hide here in the grass while I go on. Then when I've found a good place to hide I'll signal with my hand and you can advance, but off to one side."

"All right," Robert said. "I'll watch for your signal."

John went forward, slipping through the tall grass so carefully that it scarcely moved. Then he hid among some bushes and waved.

Robert slipped forward until he was some distance ahead of John and off to the right. Then he too waved his hand and hid.

In this fashion the boys moved forward across the island. Once there was no answer when John signalled Robert to advance. After waiting a moment, he croaked twice. Immediately there were two answering caws directly ahead. Robert was hidden so well that John failed to see him, and John moved so quietly that Robert failed to hear him.

After resting a while, the boys moved on, with John in the lead. Suddenly he crouched low in the grass and signalled frantically with his hand. Robert stopped. He knew at once that John had spotted danger ahead and wanted him to wait where he was.

John croaked four times to tell Robert to hide, then disappeared in the grass. Robert crouched low, hardly daring to breathe.

John crept forward cautiously on his hands and knees until he came to a kind of clearing in the bushes. A man was building a campfire in the center of the clearing, while another man was gathering dry sticks to put on the fire. Once the second man came so close that John could almost reach out and touch him.

John immediately recognized the men as the two whom he and Robert had seen smuggling the cannon through the marshland a few weeks before. The one with the red beard had a deep scar on his face and the other had a black beard and a crooked nose.

Once the fire was burning well, the black-bearded man began to get a duck ready for cooking. Evidently he had caught the duck only a short time before, because it was still limp as he held it on a stick over the fire.

Suddenly the wind changed direction and a dog began to bark angrily. Startled, John crouched lower. Then he noticed several dogs, all water spaniels, tied to some trees on the far side of the clearing.

"Make that dog stop barking!" the black-bearded man told the red-bearded one.

"Quiet, Spot!" yelled the red-beard. "You'll scare the ducks away."

The dog stopped but continued to whine and look toward the spot where John was hiding. John crept back quietly to the place where Robert was waiting and told what he had seen.

"I heard the dog," said Robert. "It scared me, a little."

"It scared me, too," John said. "I think it smelled me when the wind changed direction. These are the same men we saw dragging the cannon through the marsh a few weeks ago. They're poaching ducks now, apparently. I wish we could get a closer look at them."

"We'd better not try," said Robert.

"I think we can," John said calmly. "The wind is coming from the west now, and the dogs are tied to some trees on the southeast side of the clearing. If we hide on the north side we can watch without being caught. Come on."

He started through the grass, working his way farther to the left than before, and after a moment's hesitation Robert followed.

After they reached the clearing, they settled themselves in a safe spot and waited. Before long the duck was finished and the men ate. Then they untied the dogs and went away. The boys followed at a distance.

The men soon reached the shore of the island. Many ducks and other waterfowl were in the water, feeding or swimming about. Two flat-bottomed boats were pulled up on shore. The men divided the dogs and each got into a boat and rowed out toward the ducks. John and Robert hid at the water's edge and watched.

When the men reached the ducks, they suddenly turned the dogs loose. The dogs plunged into the water and started to seize the ducks, while the men struck at the ducks with their oars. Soon dead and injured ducks were bobbing up and down in the water.

The men gathered up the dead and injured ducks and put them in nets. All around the air was filled with cries of panic and the beating of wings.

"Let's get out of here while we can," John said. "Once those dogs stop hunting ducks they might scent us and come howling after us. Then the poachers would catch us and we might never get away from them."

The boys retreated hastily but carefully to the ridge and along the ridge to the mainland. Suddenly John realized that Robert was no longer following him. Had he slipped and fallen in the water?

John croaked twice as loudly as he dared. There was an immediate answering caw, telling him that Robert was coming, then five croaks telling him to go on to the fort. Relieved, John cawed three more times to signal that he understood, and hurried on. Soon the boys were lying on their sheepskins inside the fort.

"I never knew men could be so cruel to poor helpless birds," Robert said.

"Neither did I," said John. "I've heard of bird poaching before, but I never supposed it was anything like this."

Celebrating the Holiday Season

In December John was invited to spend the holiday season with Robert at the Willoughby manor house. While there he would visit Robert and also act as valet to Robert's younger brother. He was delighted and could scarcely wait for the holidays to come.

Mrs. Smith decided to prepare some food for John to take along. She knew that Lord Willoughby was very fond of acorn bread and pork kidney stew. His own servants seldom prepared these things for him to eat.

"Your father and I are very proud of you," she told John. "You are the first farm boy in the village to be invited to stay at the manor house. Lord Willoughby likes you."

"Well, I like Lord Willoughby, too," replied John. "He knows that Robert and I are good friends and he wants us to have good times together. He doesn't seem to mind my being a poor farmer's boy."

"Yes, I know," answered Mrs. Smith. "Lord Willoughby is a kind and generous man. We are fortunate to live on his land."

"Lord Willoughby wants me to bring a supply of peat to burn in his fireplaces during the holidays," said Mr. Smith. "John, suppose you and I hitch Dobbin to the cart and go to the bog to get a load of peat. This is a good, clear day for working outdoors."

John and his father went to the stable and hitched Dobbin to the cart. They put two shovels in the cart to use in digging and handling the peat, then climbed into the seat.

"May I drive?" John asked.

"Yes," his father replied, "but hold the lines tight. We haven't driven old Dobbin for several days and he may feel lively."

Father and son rode along in silence for some distance. Finally John said, "Why does a rich man like Lord Willoughby like to eat such things as acorn bread and pork kidney stew when he could have better things to eat? Why does he want to burn peat in his fireplaces when he has plenty of wood to burn?"

"In order to understand that you really need to know something of Lord Willoughby's early life," answered his father. "For many years Lord Willoughby was a soldier and fought in the Low Countries of Europe—in the Netherlands and Belgium. While there he learned to know and appreciate good but simple foods like pork kidney stew and acorn bread. He learned to appreciate the warmth of a good peat fire."

As they talked on, John grew a little careless in his driving. Suddenly one wheel of the cart slipped into a rut and the cart pitched sidewards, throwing Mr. Smith to the ground. John pulled tightly on the lines and clung to the seat, then jumped down to help his father. But his father was already on his feet.

Mr. Smith surveyed the accident. The only damage was a broken tug, which he quickly repaired. Then he got a pole to pry the wheel out of the rut as John urged Dobbin on. In a few moments they were on their way.

Soon they came to the peat bog and took out their shovels. The bog was a tract of low, level land composed of decayed reeds, rushes, and mosses. This material burned with a hot fire and a bright light. The top layers, called peat bags, were considered best.

Mr. Smith and John cut chunk after chunk from the surface of the ground and loaded them into the cart. Then they drove directly to Lord Willoughby's house. They had to drive slowly because the cart was heavily loaded.

At last they turned into the lane that led to the manor house. When they reached the house, several servants came out to help carry the peat bags inside. Lord Willoughby himself came to thank Mr. Smith and John.

"These look like good peat bags," he said. "There's nothing like a good peat fire for the holiday season."

During the next few days John became more anxious as he thought of his coming visit. He liked Robert and knew he would have a good time. He wondered what his duties would be as valet to Robert's younger brother. He wondered how rich people celebrated the holidays and what there would be to eat.

Mrs. Smith was filled with anxiety, too. She hoped Lord Willoughby would be pleased with the acorn bread and pork kidney stew which she would send. She worried about John's clothes, which were clean but worn and patched. She worried whether John would be polite enough and at the right times.

On the final day she packed John's clothes. By this time she was more worried than ever. Rich people from Lincolnshire and as far away as London would be Lord Willoughby's guests. What would John do in his clothes and how would he act as a valet? "He doesn't even know the duties of a valet," she said.

"Don't worry," said Mr. Smith. "John can watch how Robert does things and do them in the same way. Besides, the head servant assured me the other day that he would watch John and look after him."

When John arrived at the house, Robert was waiting to greet him. John had been there a number of times before, but he had always gone to play with Robert and had seen only a small part of the house. Now as Robert led him through the rooms he was amazed and a little frightened. Perhaps his mother had been right. How would he ever know how to act here?

First Robert took him to the big hall. At one end was a fireplace large enough for people to walk into. The walls of the room were hung with banners, flags, spears, shields, muskets, swords, and bows, all relics of Lord Willough-by's fighting in the Low Countries. High overhead big beams supported a pointed roof.

Before the fireplace stood a long oak table, dark with age, and around the table were chairs, so many chairs that John could scarcely believe his eyes. "Do that many people really eat at this table, Robert?" he asked.

Robert nodded. "Yes, but only on special occasions like Christmas. You'll see."

"That fireplace must burn a lot of wood,"

John went on. "It's so large several people could stand inside it at once."

"The servants do walk inside to clean out the ashes and to put logs on the fire," Robert replied. "But of course we only keep a fire in it when we're going to use the room. The day after Christmas, when my father gives his party, we'll have a fire in every fireplace in the house. We'll use logs and the peat you and your father brought."

As John and Robert walked about the house, John noticed that the fireplaces either had fires or were filled with logs and peat waiting to be lighted. "I'd like to see the big fireplace burning," he said. "It would be fun to light it, wouldn't it?"

"Well, maybe you can," Robert said.

"Oh, thanks—I mean, thank you, sir!"

Robert laughed. "Save your manners, John. You may need them later on."

92

The days passed quickly and John soon began to feel at home. Robert's younger brother liked him because he told interesting stories and knew a great deal about the out-of-doors. The guests and servants liked him because of his frankness and good disposition.

Mrs. Willoughby liked him, too. She ordered the servants to get him some better clothes. Soon he was wearing the same kind of clothes that Robert wore.

On Christmas morning Lord Willoughby sent for John. "My boy," he said, "on Christmas morning it is customary for the master or the son of this house to light the Yule fire in the big hall. Would you and Robert like to have that honor today?"

John was so surprised that for a moment or two he could scarcely answer. Then he managed to stammer, "I—I would consider it a great honor, my lord."

"Good," Lord Willoughby said with a smile.

With John and Robert on either side of him, he led the family and guests into the big hall. John's heart was pounding, but he felt very proud as he walked along beside Lord Willoughby dressed in his elegant clothes. Nobody would ever have suspected that he was only the son of a tenant farmer.

When they reached the fireplace John noticed that it had been filled with big logs and peat bags. On top of them was part of a log that had been burned in this same fireplace the year before. It had been carefully saved for the celebration again this year.

Everyone stood round and watched the boys as they lighted the peat bags. Flames leaped up the chimney, crackling pleasantly. Then the family and guests gathered before the fire and sang Christmas carols.

John knew that he would never forget that

day or the wonderful smells that filled the hall. In addition to the smell of woodsmoke, there were the odors of spiced foods, warm spiced drinks, and the garlands of greenery with which the hall was decorated.

And the food! John had never seen tables piled so high with all kinds of food. On a huge platter at the head of the long table lay a whole roast pig with an apple in its mouth. On another table were a roast peacock and great dishes of steaming vegetables. There were mutton pies, plum puddings, and fruits. On still another table was the great wassail bowl filled with hot spiced ale and roasted apples.

The singing stopped and the company began to eat. But even the food, rich and varied as it was, could not stop the happy conversation.

All good things come to an end, however. Before John could get used to the merriment, a man rose and called for a toast to Lord Willoughby. The toast was followed by cheers for their wonderful host.

Then somebody started to sing the "Ballad of Lord Willoughby" and all the others, Lord Willoughby excepted, joined in. The hall rang with the sound of their voices.

John and Robert stood side by side, silent and proudly erect. John didn't know many of the words, and Robert was silent because the ballad was about his father's war experiences in the Low Countries. There were three stanzas that John liked best.

"Stand to it noble pike-men
   and look you round about;
And shoot you right, you Bow-men,
   and we will keep them out:
You Musquet and Calliver men,
   do you prove true to me,
I'll be the foremost man in fight,
   says brave Lord *Willoughby.*

"And then the bloody enemy
    they fiercely did assail;
And fought it out most valiantly,
    not doubting to prevail:
The wounded men on both sides fell,
    most piteous for to see,
Yet nothing could the courage quell
    of brave Lord *Willoughby*.

"For seven hours to all men's view
    this fight endured sore,
Until our men so feeble grew,
    that they could fight no more:
And then upon dead horses
    full savourly they eat,
And drank the puddle water,
    for no better could they get."

When John went home the cottage seemed
very small, and he suddenly realized that he
had changed. He had lived briefly in a bigger,
wider world. Once more he vowed that when
he was grown he would not stay in Lincolnshire.

Troubled School Days

As A BOY John first learned to read, write, spell, and do sums at home. In those days schools were very scarce in England and were conducted only for boys. The boys' parents had to pay tuition, which was used to pay the master or teacher.

At the age of twelve, John's parents sent him to a school in Alford, which was within walking distance of home. The master of the school was a Mr. Strict, who taught all the classes. All the boys in the school were about the same age as John or a little older.

In the school there was a big wooden desk

for the teacher and a long wooden desk for the boys. The boys sat side by side on a long bench behind the desk. They learned mostly to read, write, and figure.

At first John found the school interesting and enjoyed going, but each day he had to walk through the marshland to get there. To do this was no hardship, of course, but before long he began to see things along the way that were more interesting than school. Then he began to miss school. He missed so many days that Mr. Strict finally came to the Smith home to find out why he had been absent.

When Mr. Strict arrived John was sitting on a bench under an apple tree in the yard. He suspected why Mr. Strict had come and waited for his parents to call him. In a few moments his father appeared in the doorway.

"John!"

When John entered the house his father said,

"John, Mr. Strict tells us that you have been absent from school many days. He came to see whether you have been ill or whether we have kept you home to work on the farm."

John swallowed hard but said nothing. He simply stood looking at the floor. He was in trouble and he knew it.

Mr. Smith went on. "John, have you missed school because of illness?"

"No, sir," John answered politely.

"Have we kept you at home to help work on the farm?" his father continued.

"No, sir," John replied reluctantly.

"Well, then," Mr. Smith concluded sternly, "explain your reason for being absent from school so many times these last few weeks."

John couldn't find words. "I wish I were in the middle of the marsh," he thought. "Birds and fish and flowers don't have to go to school or explain why they miss school."

"We know you stayed out of school to play," Mr. Smith went on, "but what did you do? How did you spend your time?"

Finally John recovered his voice. "Oh, I did many things," he said. "I went to the market place and listened to the fishermen talk about fishing and storms and the sea. I went to the fishing villages and learned about boats. I went to the——"

"That's enough!" Mr. Smith interrupted sharply. "You are learning the wrong things! I never had an opportunity to go to school, but I want you to get an education. I'm paying Mr. Strict for your lessons, and his fee is the same whether you go to school or not. Do you understand that?"

"Yes, sir," John replied, squirming nervously. He felt ashamed. His father worked hard to earn the money for his schooling.

"Now I want you to apologize to Mr. Strict

102

for causing him so much trouble," said Mr. Smith. "You'll no longer go to his school."

"I'm sorry for the trouble I've caused you, Mr. Strict," John said. "I just became interested in other things and didn't mean to cause you any trouble."

"That's good," said Mr. Smith. "Now I want you to hear the rest of what I have to say to Mr. Strict." He turned to Mr. Strict and added, "Sir, I too am sorry about John's behavior, but he won't cause you any more trouble. I've decided to take him out of your school and put him in a boarding school at Louth.

"Mrs. Smith and I do not believe in sparing the rod and spoiling the child," he went on. "This is Friday, but we'll spare you the task of punishing John. I'll give him a switching out in the barn tonight equal to any you might have given him in school."

Mr. Strict nodded in agreement and soon left

the house. John was still standing dejectedly in the middle of the room. He wondered what would happen next.

Mr. Smith turned to him. "John," he said, "go cut a good strong branch from the willow tree and take it to the barn. Then start to milk and feed the cows and get ready for a switching."

John looked at his mother as he started toward the door. One look convinced him that she was in complete agreement with his father. He had no choice in the matter.

Within a few days Mr. Smith took John to the boarding school in Louth. Here John had to stay away from home while he went to school. His parents thought they would no longer have trouble with his missing school.

At first John enjoyed being in Louth because there were many things to see and do there. He enjoyed the church, which had beautiful stained glass windows and carved doors and was the largest church he had ever seen. The houses were built of bricks instead of peat or plaster as they were in Willoughby, and their roofs were made of tiles instead of being thatched.

John soon grew tired of Louth, however. It lost its novelty and he found school work as boring as ever. He was lonesome for the marshes and forests and homesick for his family and Willoughby, but he didn't dare go home. Finally he began to take long walks in the countryside in search of new interests. He hiked first in one direction and then in another just to get out in the country and explore.

On some of his walks he visited villages where the people specialized in raising rabbits. He talked with the villagers and often rode back in their carts with them when they brought dressed rabbits and furs to Louth. Louth was the center of a prosperous fur industry.

At the markets in Louth John became acquainted with the fur manufacturers. He spent hours in their workshops watching the workmen dress skins. He admired their skill in cutting the furs and sewing them together to make beautiful garments.

These experts explained that many good furs came from Europe and Asia, especially Siberia. As John listened he grew even more restless and vowed again that he would visit those faraway places someday.

Every few days he went to the seacoast a few miles away. Here he mingled with the fishermen, talking with them as they prepared their daily catch for market or repaired their nets. He listened to their tales of fishing, of storms, of the lands beyond the sea.

Wherever he went, he heard people talking about strange lands in other parts of the world. Then, as he sat in the schoolroom later, he could not keep his mind on his work. He would re-

106

member the conversations and dreamily relive his excursions into the countryside.

Usually the teacher could tell by the look on John's face that he was daydreaming. The far-away look in his eyes gave him away. At such times the teacher deliberately called on him to recite, just to punish him.

Early one April morning in 1596 John went for a walk in the country before school. It was a clear, bright day, with a fresh breeze from the east. The trees were in leaf and the meadows were filled with flowers.

John strolled along, enjoying the clean air and the warm greens of the trees and grass. Suddenly he thought of school and frowned. Should he or should he not go to school today? He didn't want to go, but he probably should. The farther he walked, the more interesting the growing things around him appeared. Finally, in a flash, he made up his mind. School was no place for him. He was eager to see the world, and see the world he would.

Now that his mind was made up, he started for the fishing village to visit his friend Captain Sam. Captain Sam owned a fishing boat and had had many adventures. John hurried across the marsh so that he could visit the captain and return to Louth before dark.

When he reached the sea, John followed the shore toward the village. As he walked along, he noticed some strange, black, rocklike objects lying on the beach. Some of the objects were solid, but others crumbled in his hands when he picked them up. He put a few of the solid pieces in his pocket and hurried on.

Captain Sam was helping his men unload the fish from his boat.

"Ahoy, Captain Sam!" John called. "Ahoy!"

The captain didn't hear him and continued working. By the time John reached the boat the

captain and one of his men were lifting the last
basket out of the boat.

"Ahoy, Captain Sam!" John called again.

The captain turned a tanned and bearded
face. "Is that you, John? Come aboard."

The captain and John talked for a while. The captain suspected John had run away from school, but he said nothing. He understood the boy's love of the outdoors and wished he could help him somehow.

Finally John took one of the black objects from his pocket. "What is this?" he asked.

Captain Sam turned the object over several times in his hands, examining it. Then he crushed it into countless tiny fragments which scattered over the deck.

"Pick up some of those pieces," he said. "See how black and powdery they are."

"They look a little like soot," John said.

"This was a piece of sea coal," Captain Sam went on. "It is a kind of rock that is being mined in many parts of England now. Sometimes you can find it lying on the surface of the ground as you did this morning."

"Why do people mine it?" asked John.

"It is being used as fuel instead of peat and wood," Captain Sam explained. "It is easy to handle and gives off a great deal of heat."

"Where is it used?" asked John.

"Some people are using it to smelt iron and others are using it to make glass," Captain Sam replied. "But some scoundrels here in England are selling the stuff to Spain. The Spaniards use it to make cannons and use the cannons to fire on British ships at sea."

"The scoundrels!" cried John angrily. "They should be stopped!"

"Of course they should," the captain agreed. "They are murderers and should be punished for their deeds. They sell the sea coal for profit and make it possible for the Spaniards to shoot down our English lads. The whole thing is a blot on Queen Elizabeth's reign."

John nodded indignantly.

"I wish I were a young lad like you," the cap-

111

tain went on. "I'd join one of the Queen's great captains and go off in search of adventure. I'd have given a great deal to be with Sir Francis Drake when he sailed around the world, or with Sir Walter Raleigh's men when they tried to plant a colony in America. England may be proud of such men, my boy!"

John's eyes shone. "Nothing would suit me better than to sail off to explore strange parts of the world," he said.

"Well, lad, you would make a good sailor, and you are old enough," the captain said. "England needs good sailors and soldiers. Spain has sent many men and ships to explore and conquer the world, especially in America. We must do the same. We must build more ships and enlist more men to combat her."

By the time John left Captain Sam that afternoon he had made up his mind that he was old enough to start exploring the world. He would hurry home to tell his father and mother about his decision. They would be sorry, he knew, but after all they were wasting their money in sending him to school.

He started immediately, but when he reached home he discovered that his father had died only a few hours before. He was so shocked that he forgot about his plans.

George Smith had left a will, dated March 30, 1596. One paragraph read as follows:

"To the Right Honorable, my Lord Willoughby, under whom I many years lived as a poor tenant, as a token of my dutiful good will, I leave the best of my two year colts. I give and leave to Alice, my wife, the farm which I now dwell in which I hold by copy of court Royal by a grant of the Right Honorable my aforesaid good Lord, during her widowhood according to the custom of his Lordship's custom of Willoughby; and if it please God that my said wife do marry again and take a second husband, then my will is that my said farm shall come to John Smith, my eldest son who I charge and I command to honor and love my good Lord Willoughby during his life."

John listened to the reading of the will with mixed feelings. He honored and respected Lord Willoughby and he loved his mother, but he was certain that he would never be content to stay on the farm the rest of his life.

The Unhappy Apprentice

JOHN STOOD on top of a small haystack near the milkshed, pitching hay down to the ground. Suddenly he drove his pitchfork into the hay, leaned on it, and gazed toward the east. There lay the sea and the great world beyond—a far more exciting world than the farm with its haystacks and fields.

John's mother came from the house. As she approached the shed, she studied John. He was staring eastward as if in a trance. She rattled the milk pails, but he did not notice the sound. His baby sister fell and started to cry. The cows mooed and a rooster crowed loudly somewhere in the barnyard, but John did not budge or seem to notice.

Finally Mrs. Smith said, "A penny for your thoughts, John."

There was no answer.

John was not impolite. He was just so deep in thought that he did not hear her.

Ever since Mr. Smith's death a few months before, John had tried to fill his father's shoes. He knew that people expected him to help his mother. He knew that they expected him to live and work on the farm for the rest of his life, just as his father had done. As the days and weeks passed, however, he had come to realize that he could not stay. He had not been born to work on a farm.

At the time of his father's death, he had heard two neighbors talking.

"The poor boy stopped going to school in Louth just to help his mother," one remarked.

"Yes," said the other. "Isn't it fortunate that the widow Smith has a big strong son to take his father's place?"

John didn't tell them that he had not quit school to help his mother but to run away to sea. He didn't tell them that he had returned to Willoughby only to get a few things and to see his family before leaving. He didn't tell them anything.

Now he was faced with a problem for which he could find no answer. He hated farm work and wanted to leave, but at the same time he felt sorry for his mother. It didn't seem right to leave her with all the work.

Just the same, he felt caged in. The farm was so small! He could plow in the fields all day and not lose sight of the cottage. A bird flying overhead could be a mile away before he turned the team around.

John thought of his childhood, when he had

no greater responsibility than to herd the geese with Big Jack. He had been free to play in the marshes then, but now——

"John! Do you see a ship coming in?"

The word "ship" brought him to with a start and he looked down from the haystack to find his mother smiling at him.

"Pitch down some hay," she said. "As soon as I finish milking, I'll fix frumenty, eggs, apple fritters, and warm milk."

"Good!" he said, taking up the pitchfork again. "I'm hungry." He loved frumenty, which was a kind of stew made of wheat, currants, raisins, and spices boiled in milk.

"You're always hungry!" his mother laughed. "It takes a lot of food to fill you."

That evening after supper John stretched out before the fireplace. This was his favorite time of the day and the hearth was his favorite spot. The warmth of the fire felt good after his long

118

hours in the fields, and the flames took on the shapes of his dreams.

Mrs. Smith brought a stool to the hearth and sat beside him. "John, your guardians will be here tomorrow evening," she said.

John sat up quickly and turned his back to the fire. "Why?"

"I can see you do not like farm work," she replied. "You will never be a good farmer, no matter how hard you try. For that reason, I believe you should work in a town. I have asked your guardians to come so we can discuss your future. If you were apprenticed to a merchant you might get to travel to those faraway lands you dream about so often."

"Who will do the work here, Mother?" he asked. "You can't get along without help."

"Don't worry," she said confidently. "I know where I can get a hired man."

John hesitated a moment, then said slowly,

"It doesn't seem right to go off and leave you alone on the farm, but you're right, Mother. I hate farming. I'll always hate it. And I would like to see the world."

Two weeks later Mrs. Smith and John's guardians had arranged for John to become an apprentice to Thomas Sendall. Mr. Sendall was a wool merchant who lived in King's Lynn, a seaport about sixty miles from Willoughby. He bought and sold wool and shipped it to foreign countries in his own ships.

John was delighted. He saw himself going to sea soon in one of Mr. Sendall's ships.

John's first weeks in King's Lynn were happy ones. The seaport was a busy place, with ships coming and going at all times. Outbound ships carried wool and woolen cloth. Inbound ships brought furs from Russia, silk and linen cloth from Italy and the Low Countries, glass from Venice, and news from everywhere.

Some of the news was good and some bad, but it was all exciting. For example, John learned that Sir Francis Drake was dead. Drake had been the first Englishman to sail around the world and was one of Captain Sam's heroes.

John also heard that an English fleet had attacked the great Spanish seaport of Cadiz. The fleet had destroyed forty Spanish merchant ships and thirteen warships, and had burned the port. This daring adventure would help Queen Elizabeth and England win the war against King Philip of Spain.

John also heard people talking about the Queen's favorite, Sir Walter Raleigh. Sir Walter had just returned from a voyage up the Orinoco River in northern South America. He was publishing a book about his discoveries there, in which he urged the English people to go out and settle in faraway lands. John was already eager and ready to go.

John's work was not difficult and he learned it quickly. Unfortunately, it kept him in Mr. Sendall's warehouse most of the time, and he found it boring, too. Being caged in a warehouse was worse than being caged in a field. Such a life was not what he had hoped for and he began to grow discontented again.

One day he was called to Mr. Sendall's counting room or office. "I must send a message to the captain of my ship, the 'Endeavor,' at once," Mr. Sendall said. "Do you know where she is docked?"

"No, sir, but I can find her," John said eagerly. "I'll go at once."

"Give him this and wait for an answer," said Mr. Sendall, handing John a note.

"Yes, sir!" John took the note and headed for the door.

"And come back at once!" Mr. Sendall called after him. "No dallying!"

122

John hurried through the narrow streets until he came to the waterfront. There the cobblestoned quays were lined with ships whose bare masts and spars resembled a forest of crosses. Sailors thronged the quays, loading and unloading cargoes, while others prepared their vessels for their next voyage to sea.

John found the "Endeavor" and gave the captain his message. While waiting for an answer, he talked with some of the sailors who were carrying bales of fleeces aboard.

"Where are you bound?" he asked.

"To Russia," one said.

Russia! The word brought pictures to John's mind of the dark forests and vast grasslands that were said to cover the lands of the Russians. "I wish I could go," he said.

At that moment the captain returned. "You'd better be getting this back to Master Sendall," he said abruptly. "He'll not be liking it if you

123

dawdle on the way. Be off with you now, and quick! We've work to do before we sail."

John sighed. "That's what Mr. Sendall told me when I left," he said. "Be quick!"

When John returned to the counting room, he had to wait for Mr. Sendall to finish some business. The captain of another of Mr. Sendall's ships was waiting, too. He was standing before a large map of the world that hung on the wall, studying it carefully.

"Look at that," he said as John approached him, and pointed to one section of the map. "This was a fine map when Sebastian Cabot made it in 1544, but he knew little about the New World. I sailed around the world with Drake in the 'Golden Hind' and I know the coast of the Americas is not like that." He shook his head. "We have learned a great deal about the world since Cabot's time, my lad, but there is still much to learn."

John looked at the map, fascinated. It was beautiful, but he was sure the captain was right. There was much to learn about the world, many unknown lands to explore. And John Smith would be one of the explorers!

When Mr. Sendall finally called him in, John blurted, "Send me to sea, sir!"

Mr. Sendall laughed. "You're only a boy. Wait till you become a man."

John didn't want to wait. He was only seventeen, but he was sure that he was as intelligent and strong and brave as any man. He wouldn't wait! He would go now!

After that, John spent more and more time along the waterfront, watching the ships and talking with the sailors. He neglected his work and became careless and dreamy.

One day as John was staring at a map, lost in thought, Mr. Sendall called, "John, did you move those fleeces into the warehouse?"

John was so absorbed in his dreams that he heard nothing.

"Young man!" Mr. Sendall seized him by the arm. "Why don't you work as well as you did the first few weeks you were here?"

"I'll do better if you'll send me to sea on one of your ships," John said.

Mr. Sendall's face grew red and he spluttered and choked with anger. "Ships! Sea! Don't you think of anything else? How can I make a merchant of a lad who thinks of nothing but the sea? Well, let me tell you, young man, I'll ship you if you don't tend to work. I'll ship you back to Willoughby and you can find your adventure there!"

John Goes to France

DRESSED in their best clothes, John and his mother strolled along the lane that led to Lord Willoughby's manor house. It was a fine summer day, with a fresh breeze stirring the leaves of the trees and larks singing high over the meadows and fields.

John had returned to Willoughby, with Mr. Sendall's permission, to see his guardians and gain release from his apprenticeship. He and his mother were going to the manor house to meet his guardians now and to discuss the matter with Lord Willoughby. John hoped they would give him permission to go to sea.

"Lord Willoughby will do what he thinks is best for you," John's mother said. "He likes you, son. He thinks you have a good mind and many good qualities, but he also thinks you are head-strong and brash."

"Maybe I am," John said, "but I am strong enough to do a man's work and it is a man's work I want to do."

"I know," said his mother, a little sadly. "But Lord Willoughby has traveled and fought in Europe and knows how cruel the world can be to a young man."

"I'm not afraid of the world, Mother," John said confidently.

The manor house did not seem quite so large and fine to John as it once had. His few months in King's Lynn had already shown him something of the world.

Lord Willoughby gave John a friendly welcome. He told him that Robert was studying in

Orleans, France. "I am sending his brother Peregrine and a tutor to Orleans, too. Since your guardians feel you are too young to go to sea, I have offered to send you along as Peregrine's page. Would you like that?"

John was delighted. At last he would visit a foreign land!

He loved Orleans. Its narrow twisting streets and its buildings and people were different from those of Lincolnshire. However, he found so much to see that he soon became slack in his duties, as he had at King's Lynn. When he was sent on an errand he would not return for hours. He wandered about the streets, watching, listening, talking, and soon he spoke better French than Peregrine himself.

At last the latter's tutor, annoyed, gave him money for the journey back to Willoughby and dismissed him.

John took the money and went to Paris. One

day as he was walking along a street he heard a voice call, "How are things in England, my young friend?"

John whirled around, astonished. How did anyone know that he was from England?

A man behind him smiled. "Yes, I am speaking to you, young man. I know the look of an Englishman. I traveled through England on my way here from Scotland. My name is Hume, David Hume, and I long for news from home. Sometimes I grow tired of hearing and speaking only French. What part of England are you from, my fine young friend?"

"I am John Smith of Lincolnshire, at your service, sir," John said.

"Lincolnshire! Then you have heard of the famous Lord Willoughby."

"Yes, sir, I know Lord Willoughby," John said proudly. "Do you?"

"He is an old friend of my family and I fought

with him briefly in the Low Countries," David Hume replied.

David Hume and John soon became close friends. Hume was an interesting man who knew Paris well, but he had a big appetite and little money. Their meals were always paid for from John's rapidly dwindling supply. At first John didn't mind, for he enjoyed Mr. Hume, but before long he became worried.

When Hume learned that John's money was almost gone, he said smoothly, "John, I have enjoyed showing you Paris, but I must go now. I have just received orders from King James of Scotland sending me on a special mission to Switzerland."

Before John could recover from the shock of this information, Hume went on, "I have written some letters of introduction to influential friends of mine in Scotland. These friends will introduce you to other friends in Edinburgh who can help you to obtain a good position in the King's court. Guard these letters with your life, my boy. They are of great value."

As John hesitated, Hume continued, "My boy, I haven't sealed one of them. Let me read you what I have written."

Mr. Hume read part of a letter which described John in glowing words. Then he shook John's hand. "Goodby, my boy."

Bewildered by this sudden change in Hume's attitude, John set off for the English Channel. When he reached it, he discovered that he did not have enough money left to pay his passage back to England. He was stranded in a strange city in a foreign land, without money, relatives, or friends.

Discouraged, he wandered along the waterfront, wondering what to do. Suddenly the great world beyond the sea did not seem so fascinating or so friendly.

Once he heard some sailors speaking English and he approached their captain and offered to work for his passage home. When the captain learned that John had never been to sea he shook his head and continued with his work. John wandered on, more discouraged than ever. What now? Could he stow away on a ship bound for England?

Suddenly he heard music in a nearby square and went to investigate. A crowd had gathered around some musicians and a young army officer, who began to address them in Dutch.

"What is he saying?" John asked a bystander in French.

"He is asking for volunteers in the Dutch army," the bystander replied. "The army needs men to carry on the war against Spain."

John's spirits rose. Here was a double opportunity—a chance for adventure and a chance to earn money for his journey to Scotland. He stepped forward boldly. "I will volunteer," he said in English.

"You are English?" asked the officer.

"From Lincolnshire," answered John.

"The great Lord Willoughby was from Lincolnshire," the officer said. "Anyone from his country is welcome here."

John fought in Holland and saved his pay. During all his fighting he carefully protected the letters from David Hume. He was sure that when he reached Scotland they would help him obtain a good position at court.

When his enlistment was over, he left Holland on the first ship for Scotland. His heart sang as he felt the cold wind of the North Sea in his face and heard the waves slapping against the bow of the ship. Nobody could say now that he was not a man. He had traveled abroad and was just as much a veteran of the wars as Lord Willoughby himself.

When the ship reached the Isle of Lindisfarne, off northern England, a storm arose. The wind howled, the ship pitched and rolled and was finally wrecked. Many passengers drowned in the icy water, but John was a strong swimmer and managed to reach shore.

He was found on the beach the next morning, exhausted and nearly dead from exposure. He was ill for weeks, but when he recovered the islanders took him ashore and gave him money to continue his journey to Scotland.

At last he reached the town to which David Hume had told him to go. It was a small place, one narrow street lined with small cottages with thatched roofs. On a hill above the town was a manor house resembling the home of Lord Willoughby.

Stopping the first person he met, John showed him the letters from David Hume. "Where might I find the home of the Right Honorable Andrew McLean?" he asked politely. "I have some letters for him."

The man pointed up the hill. "Yonder. He'll be there now."

The door of the mansion opened at John's knock and a servant appeared.

"I have a letter for Mr. McLean from David Hume of Paris," John said.

"This way, sir." The servant led him to a room where a tall lean man in a kilt stood warming himself before a fire. His face was craggy and his hair long and white. He greeted John politely. "What may I do for you, sir?"

John watched him as he read the letter from David Hume. It was obvious that he liked what he read, but when he had finished and glanced hastily through the others he frowned and shook his head.

"I see our friend has not changed his ways," he said sadly. "No doubt he gave you these letters after borrowing money that he did not pay back."

"Well—yes, sir, he did."

"I thought so. David means well, but he is not quite honest. He owes me more money than he could pay back if he worked all the rest of

138

his life. Besides that, things have changed here in Scotland. David's friends are no longer influential at court and cannot help you. I am sorry. If we could, we would. I am sure you deserve all the praise that David has given you, but times have changed."

John's heart sank. Had he come all the way to Scotland, and nearly lost his life, to hear this? "What shall I do?" he asked.

Mr. McLean shook his head. "I cannot help you at court, but if you wish, my friends and I can help you return to your home."

"That would be good of you, sir," John said gratefully. "I will accept your offer."

So it was that after four years in Europe and Scotland, John returned to Willoughby. Nothing had changed. The little church was the same, the streets and houses were the same, and the fields were as small and neatly hedged as ever. As he followed the lane that led to the cottage in which he had been born, the children stared. His clothes were strange and his face was unfamiliar. His sister, seated in the doorway, stared with disbelief.

"John! John!" she cried, running forward to throw her arms around him. "Where in the world have you been? We thought you were dead."

"Welcome home, John," his brother said, grasping him by the hand.

"I'm glad to be home," John said with a smile.

Captain John Smith

THINGS HAD changed in Willoughby, John soon learned. His mother was dead and his younger brother was managing the farm. The forests and marshes in which he had played as a boy seemed smaller than before, and so did the village and the fields surrounding it.

All John's boyhood friends were married and had children. Since they had never been more than fifty miles from Willoughby, they wanted to hear about his adventures. As a result, he was very popular for a while because he brought news of faraway places.

When Lord Willoughby learned that John had

returned, John was invited to the manor house. He told of his experiences in Orleans with Robert and Peregrine and about his fighting in the Low Countries. Then he told about his journey to Scotland.

"What do you plan to do now?"

"I'd like to be a soldier," John said, "but I have learned that I must know more. I must learn to ride a horse and handle weapons, and how to command men."

"Perhaps I can help you," said Lord Willoughby. "I can lend you books on warfare, and I know a man who can teach you how to ride a horse and handle weapons."

Thus it happened that John moved into a small cottage near home and spent the following months studying and practicing. He worked harder than he had ever worked before and at last came to feel that he had learned something about warfare.

By this time he was growing restless again and returned to France. His riding teacher had told him about the war which the Christian rulers of eastern Europe were waging against the Turks, and John decided to join them.

When he reached southern France, he could find no way to reach the fighting, so instead he joined the crew of a ship bound for Egypt. For months the ship sailed eastward, stopping at ports in Africa, Egypt, and eastern Mediterranean countries. At last, on the homeward voyage, it met a richly laden merchant vessel from the city of Venice.

In those days piracy was common and the ships of foreign countries were considered fair prey, even for honest sailors. The French attacked, the Italians returned the fire, and a fierce battle occurred. When it ended, the Italian ship lay helpless.

Transferring the rich cargo to their own ship,

the French sailed for home. John's share of the booty seemed a small fortune to him.

Next he traveled to Italy, and from Italy to Hungary, where he finally joined the Christian army fighting the Turks. The Turks had conquered Constantinople and had invaded Greece and Hungary and were threatening middle Europe. For years the Christians had struggled to drive them out, with little success.

Young Smith's help was welcomed. When the Turks surrounded a city and cut it off from the Christian army, he went to his commanding officer and said, "If the army inside the city attacks and we attack at the same time, we can drive the Turks away."

"True," said the general, "but we cannot get a message through the Turkish lines."

"I can send it by means of signal fires," Smith said. "Let me try."

He got the message through and the Turks

were driven off. As a reward, John Smith was made a captain and put in command of two hundred and fifty horsemen.

Later he fought and won three duels with the best horsemen in the Turkish army. For these victories he was given rich clothing, arms, and equipment for his horses.

A day came, however, when the Turkish army defeated the Hungarians. Smith was severely wounded and left for dead. He was found by some Turkish soldiers who were robbing the bodies of arms and clothes.

Thinking he was a nobleman, the soldiers decided to ransom him. They nursed him until he was well, then demanded money for his release. They were furious when he told them, laughing, that he was only a farm boy from England. They took his possessions, dressed him in rags, and sold him as a slave.

The Turkish officer who bought Smith sent

him to Constantinople as a present for his future wife. This young woman felt sorry for him and sent him to her brother, who managed a big estate or farm in southern Russia.

Smith expected to be put in charge of the other slaves on the estate. When he arrived, however, his hair and beard were shaved off and an iron collar was riveted around his neck. Then he was put to work in the fields along with many other slaves.

Within a few months' time he had fallen from the rank of captain in the Hungarian army to that of a Russian slave. As he looked at his fellow slaves, ragged and half dead with fatigue and hunger, he felt bitter. Why had this happened to him? He would rather be dead than be a slave! Nevertheless, he would not give up. He knew somehow, deep inside, that his luck would change. Nobody would keep him in slavery for long!

146

As the long months passed, Smith endured a great deal. Then one day, when he was working in a field alone, his master began to whip him unmercifully. Smith's temper exploded. Pulling the man from his horse, Smith killed him with his bare hands.

Suddenly he realized that his opportunity had come. He put on the man's clothing and buried his body. Then, taking the horse and some food from the warehouse, he fled. He was not sure where he was, but he knew that he could reach safety by traveling northwest and he set off in that direction.

He traveled for two weeks, hiding by day and moving only at night. At last he came to a city on the Don River in a part of Russia that was controlled by the Russians themselves. His story was so fantastic that the governor of the town would not believe it at first, in spite of the iron collar around Smith's neck.

"Perhaps you are nothing but a Russian criminal," said the governor doubtfully.

"Would I know English, French, and Italian if I were a Russian peasant?" Smith asked. "Would I know about the war in Hungary?"

The governor did not answer. He gave a command in Russian and Smith was led away. Finally, however, the collar was removed and he was given food and clothing and allowed to rest. Then he was allowed to continue his journey toward the Baltic Sea.

In Leipzig, Germany, he met Prince Sigismund Bathori, for whom he had fought in Hungary. When he told the prince what had happened to him, the prince gave him a large sum of money and a safe-conduct pass with the prince's seal on it. The last two paragraphs of the pass read as follows:

"We request therefore of all our dearest and nearest dukes, earls, princes, governors of towns or ships in this territory or any other provinces in which he shall endeavor to come, that this Captain may be permitted to pass freely without hindrance. Which doing with all kindness we shall always do the like for you.

"Sealed in Leipzig (Lesprizea) in Misen the 9th day of December, in the year of our Lord 1603."

Now that he was supplied with money and the prince's pass, John could have returned to England, but he didn't. Once more the urge for travel and adventure lured him on, and he spent two more years wandering about Europe.

He visited various German states and returned to the Low Countries, where he had first fought against the Spanish. Then he returned across northern France to Paris, where he hunted David Hume but failed to find him. From Paris he went south to Spain and Portugal, and then by ship to northwest Africa.

Finally, after a second four-year period away from home, he started for England in 1604. During those four years he had traveled in more countries and rubbed elbows with more lords and princes than most men did in a lifetime. He had left home plain John Smith to seek adventure and make a name for himself. Now he was returning to England a captain in the Hungarian army with gold in his purse. He had a right to be satisfied, he felt.

He didn't know that still more travel and adventure awaited him in faraway lands.

Home Again

THE SHIP was docked and Captain John Smith peered eagerly through the fog for a glimpse of London. He knew the city was there, but the fog was so thick that he could see nothing. Nevertheless, he was glad to be home. He had been away long enough.

His mind was filled with memories of the England of his youth, and he longed to see the familiar scenes of Willoughby. He longed for news of his family and friends.

Gathering his things, he left the ship and strode briskly but carefully down the street. He paused now and then to shift his burden or to look with interest at the wares displayed in a shop window. Then he hurried on in search of a decent-looking inn.

Suddenly he heard loud, quarrelsome voices somewhere ahead of him. He could not see the speakers in the fog, but they seemed to be coming his way.

Rather than run into the group, he stepped into a shop entrance. The door opened slightly and a voice said softly, "Stranger, I suggest you step inside before that herd of beggars runs over you."

"Thank you, sir," Smith replied, slipping through the door. A bald little man peered at him through spectacles. Leaving the door open slightly, Smith looked out.

Then he saw the beggars. Unwashed, ragged, with piercing eyes and clawlike hands, they swept along the street in search of scraps of food or clothing. As Smith watched, two of them began to fight over a half-rotten apple and several others struggled for possession of a piece of discarded clothing. They reminded Smith of rats that he had seen fighting over scraps of food on a ship.

Suddenly two of the beggars noticed the half-open door and lunged toward it. Quickly Smith slammed the door shut and lowered the bar that locked it.

"Thank you for your quick thinking, stranger," the shopkeeper said.

"Thank you for inviting me in. Isn't it safe for an Englishman to walk alone on the streets these days?"

"Not if he looks prosperous and has obviously just returned from abroad," the shopkeeper answered. "Not in London anyhow. Sit down, sir, and rest a while."

The two sat down and eyed each other for a few moments. At last Smith said, "Why does the government permit such men on the streets? What is happening here?"

"Those men are licensed beggars," the shopkeeper said. "The government has given them a permit to beg."

"But they act like thieves!"

"They do. They are so cold and hungry they would rob or even kill to get clothes and money," said the shopkeeper.

"Why don't they work?" Smith's voice was scornful and his eyes flashed with anger.

"Stranger——"

"Captain Smith from Lincolnshire, sir."

"Well, Captain, may I ask if you have just arrived in London?"

"Yes," Smith said. "Why do you ask?"

"I thought so. You don't seem to know what has happened in England since Queen Elizabeth died." The shopkeeper shook his head sadly and added, "I was about to eat my breakfast,

Captain. Perhaps, since you have just returned to England, you would like to share a good English breakfast with me."

Smith accepted the invitation eagerly. As the two men ate, the shopkeeper explained that conditions in England were very bad. The war with Spain had ended and many returning soldiers had been unable to find work. Some were sick, some crippled, and many others were hungry and dissatisfied, he said.

After listening to the shopkeeper's story, Smith rose. "Sir," he said, "I have enjoyed your breakfast. I would like to pay for it if you do not object."

"I did not invite you in to make a profit," the old man said, "but I must admit that I could use the money."

John gave him some coins. "I suppose conditions are better in the country than they are here in London?"

156

The old man shook his head. "No, about the same. There's not enough work in England for all our people."

John took his change. He had planned to stay in London for a few days, but suddenly he was eager to get to Willoughby and home. He had had enough of gloom, misery, unhappiness, and danger. He wanted to see the farm and talk with his brother and sister, and he could not leave London soon enough.

Gathering up his things, he opened the door and hurried into the fog.

A few days later he reined in his horse in front of the cottage at Willoughby. His sister Alice was sitting in the doorway as his mother used to do.

"John! John Smith!" she cried, rushing forward to throw her arms around his neck. "We really thought you were dead this time!"

That evening after supper John Smith sat before the fireplace with his sister and brother and his brother's family. His nieces and nephews fought for a chance to sit on his lap.

"Tell us another story, Uncle John! Tell us another!" they shouted.

"Uncle John is tired, children," Alice said at last. "He has traveled a long way today. He can tell you more stories tomorrow."

"No, I'll tell you one more story if you will all promise to go to bed without complaining when I'm finished," John said.

Shouts of "Yes, yes! I will! We will!" filled the cottage.

After the children were sent to bed, the grownups talked.

"You look prosperous, John," his brother said. "Things must have gone well for you."

"And you've grown. You look so much bigger and stronger than you used to," Alice added.

"How is the farming?" John asked.

"We're getting by," his brother said. "So far, we've managed to get enough to eat, but that's about all. Times are hard."

"That's more than many people have in the cities," John said. Then, thinking of the misery he had seen, he added, "At least you have enough to eat and something to wear. You are all well. That wasn't true of the people I saw in London. They're starving there."

Presently the women left the room and John muttered, "I must find work."

His brother looked up in amazement. "John, this is your land. You know you can stay here as long as you wish."

"I know, but I must find something to do. I can't sit around here doing nothing like a lazy dog," John said.

His brother was puzzled. "There isn't any work available, John, no matter what you would like to do. Still, if you would like to keep busy, you can help me with the work on the farm. There's plenty of that."

"It's strange," John said. "The people in France and Spain are not as poor as people here. Why are Englishmen starving when the French and Spanish are not?"

That night John couldn't sleep. He kept thinking about France and Spain, England's rivals. What made them more prosperous than England? What did they do or have that kept their people at work?

Suddenly an idea came to him. Seaports! London had not been busy when he arrived a few days ago, but the seaports of France and Spain were as busy as beehives. They were crowded with ships bringing gold, silver, furs, lumber, fish, and many other products from overseas—from the New World!

John sat up in bed. Now he knew the answer—colonies. France and Spain had colonies

in the New World which were making them prosperous. England had no colonies. If she were to establish some, her people too would have opportunities for work and trade.

In his excitement, John got up and walked about the room. Now he knew what he wanted to do. He would convince people in authority that England should establish colonies.

After a brief visit with his family, he returned to London. There he talked with people high and low, explaining his ideas. A few people believed him, but many did not.

One day he met his old friend Robert Bertie, son of Lord Willoughby. Lord Willoughby was dead now and Robert had succeeded to his father's title, lands, and position. After hearing of John's adventures, Robert asked him what he planned to do.

John began to talk enthusiastically about his dreams. When he finished, Robert said thoughtfully, "It's strange that you should say these things. I have a friend, Bartholomew Gosnold, who believes as you do. In fact, he and some of his friends are organizing a company to establish a colony in Raleigh's Virginia. I must give you a letter to him."

Armed with this letter, John went to see Bartholomew Gosnold.

"Do you seek a fortune in Virginia, Smith?" Gosnold asked.

"I would like to earn something," John replied, "but I believe England will prosper only if we can plant colonies in America. I want to see those colonies succeed!"

Sir Bartholomew smiled. "Smith, you and I can work together. Would you like to join us?"

"I would, sir!" John exclaimed.

There and then John Smith of Willoughby, farmer boy and Captain in the Hungarian army, became a member of the Virginia Company. From that point on, his life was devoted to the exploration and development of the New World. He had found the work for which all his past experiences had prepared him.

Jamestown

"LAND HO!" In the crow's nest high above the deck of the ship the lookout pointed and shouted again. "Land dead ahead!"

Below, Captain John Smith and others of the Virginia Company who were sailing aboard the "Susan Constant" rushed to the ship's rail. When they saw the shoreline in the distance, a cheer of triumph arose. The long voyage across the Atlantic was over at last.

Captain Smith turned to the master of the "Susan Constant." "Well, Captain Newport," he said, "you have brought us here safely. Now the real task begins."

Captain Newport frowned. "I have no map of this coast. We had better anchor in the mouth of the bay until we can learn how deep the water is." He gave an order and the sailors soon brought the ship into the mouth of a wide bay and dropped anchor. The two smaller ships carrying the rest of the Virginia settlers anchored close by.

Immediately the ship's carpenters began to put together a smaller boat called a shallop. It was equipped with oars and sails and could be used in shallow water.

While this was being done, Captain Smith and the other settlers studied the shore through their spyglasses. Beyond the sandy beach lay a dark, unbroken forest.

At last the shallop was finished. "Who will volunteer to help take the shallop into the bay and find a channel for the ships?" asked Captain Newport.

The men hesitated. They were afraid to go first, afraid of the unknown.

At last Captain Smith stepped forward. "I'll be happy to go, sir."

"What if we find Indians in there?" whispered several men.

"We'll use sign language," Smith said. "One of the things I learned during my years of traveling and fighting in Europe is that men of different countries can understand sign language. We'll have no trouble."

Others volunteered then and the shallop was soon on its way. In a few days it returned with news that a good place for the settlement had been discovered. Smith and Bartholomew Gosnold, in the shallop, led the ships into Chesapeake Bay and up a broad river which they had named the James. They stopped at a place where the river was deep enough for the ships to be brought close to shore.

"We're far enough inland here that pirates or French and Spanish ships will never find us," Smith said.

Going ashore, the men started to build a settlement. Much work was required to clear away the brush and cut the larger trees. Some of the trees were used to make a fort, while others were cut into lumber and loaded on the "Susan Constant" to be sent home.

A few weeks later, in May, 1607, John Smith went exploring for the first time. He and Captain Newport and several others took the shallop up the James River, where no white man had ever gone before. As the shallop moved cautiously upstream, Smith made sketches of the shoreline and took notes of the many strange and interesting things he saw.

From time to time Indians appeared, and the Englishmen stopped to trade with them. They gave pocket knives, spears, bells, beads, and glass trinkets for oysters, deer meat, berries, nuts, beans, corn, fish, tobacco, and various other things. Smith became so good at trading that he won the respect of both the Indians and his white companions.

When they reached a falls in the river, they found an Indian village. The chief of the village invited them to stay. He told them about the falls and the land above it. Each night he held a feast and invited other Indians to meet the white men.

After several days, Smith called Captain Newport to one side. "Sir," he said, "I'm suspicious of these Indians. Why are they giving us a feast each night? And why are messengers coming and going every day? I'm sure they carry messages up and down the river."

Captain Newport was alert at once. "Go on, Smith," he said. "You have an idea. What do you think the savages are planning?"

168

"Well, sir, in eastern Europe and Asia feasting is often used as a trick. It is a way of dividing a group of men into two parts so that each part is easier to attack. What if the Indians are planning to attack the settlement while we are feasted here?"

"Hm-m-m." Captain Newport stroked his beard and stared thoughtfully at the river. "We'll start home in the morning."

Later that day Newport, Smith, and the others erected a cross at the falls of the James River, claiming the river and all the land it drained for King James of England. The next morning they left for Jamestown.

Before they could reach the settlement, however, the Indians attacked it. Many Indians were killed, and some Englishmen as well, but the attack was driven off and the settlement saved. By the time the explorers reached the settlement the danger was past.

When he reported to the governing committee on the results of his expedition, Captain Newport praised Smith highly. Without him, he said, the expedition could hardly have succeeded. As a reward, Smith was made a member of the committee.

Within a few weeks the fort was completed and the crops were planted. Then, in June, Captain Newport sailed for England in the "Susan Constant" with a load of lumber. One hundred and five men were left in Jamestown.

Summer came, bringing hot, sticky weather. Many of the men—the "gentlemen," as John Smith called them scornfully—refused to work. They would not work in the fields or fish or hunt for meat, preferring to loaf, quarrel, or hunt gold. Worms got into the flour and spoiled it, and food ran low. Swarms of mosquitoes from near-by swamps attacked the men day and night. By September, forty men had died.

During that terrible summer the colony's situation went from bad to worse, but from it all one fact emerged. The real leader of the settlement was not President Wingfield or Sir Bartholomew Gosnold or any of the other fine gentlemen adventurers. It was John Smith, the farmer's son, the same strong, determined, driving John Smith who had always refused to surrender, no matter what the odds.

When the settlement needed food, he would take the shallop and a group of men and go off on a trading expedition. He would bring back enough oysters, fish, turkey, fowls, bread, and corn to last the settlers for several weeks. When food ran low again, he would make another trip in a different direction.

While trading, he also explored the rivers that emptied into Chesapeake Bay. He made sketches and took notes so that he could make a map of the country.

On one trip Smith and his men were attacked by Indians and Smith was captured. Already his reputation had spread among the Indians. He was taken from village to village like a wild animal so that the children and women could see what he looked like. Some of the children would reach out to touch his skin with their fingers. They wanted to see whether the white would rub off.

Smith learned enough of the Indians' language so that he could talk with them. One day his captors offered to set him free if he would show them how to capture Jamestown and kill the settlers. They said he could marry an Indian girl and spend the rest of his life with them in their village.

Smith hesitated. He didn't trust his captors and knew they wouldn't live up to any promise they made, so he decided to outwit them. Finally he nodded.

"Very well. I'll help you if you'll first send a letter to Jamestown for me."

The Indians had no writing and therefore did not know what a letter was. He explained in the letter that the Indians planned to attack the settlement, and he asked President Wingfield to give the messenger several gifts for the Indian chief.

Then, as he handed the letter to the chief, he said, "If this letter is delivered to the white chief in Jamestown, he will send you many fine gifts. If it is not delivered, he will know that you have not kept your word and will punish you."

The messenger hurried to Jamestown and returned with the gifts Smith had promised. The chief was surprised and pleased—and somewhat worried. He began to fear that Smith was a dangerous spirit and decided to take him to his brother, Powhatan, the chief of all the tribes

in that part of the country. He set out with Smith for Powhatan's village.

Like his brother, Powhatan was impressed. He was impressed by the compass Smith carried and by Smith's talk about the sun, moon, and stars and his powerful lord, the King of England. But he too was afraid that Smith was a dangerous spirit and finally ordered him killed.

Smith's arms were tied behind his back and he was stretched out on the ground, with his head on a big rock. Then painted warriors with war clubs began to dance around him. The dance grew faster and the shouts of the watchers grew louder and more frenzied.

Smith lay quiet as the dance went on. If his end had come, he would die like a man.

Suddenly, just as the dance reached its peak and Powhatan raised his hand to signal, Pocahontas rushed forward and threw herself on the stone beside Smith.

175

"Spare him, father!" she cried. "Spare him for me!"

The dancers stopped and Powhatan rose to his feet, astonished. Finally he cried, "Free the prisoner! My daughter has asked for his life and her wish is granted."

John Smith breathed a deep and trembling sigh of relief.

When he returned to the settlement later, he found it in desperate trouble. Little food was left and only thirty-eight men remained alive. Fortunately, Captain Newport arrived from England the very next day, bringing food, supplies, and more men, and the colony was saved.

The two captains, Newport and Smith, spent that spring trading with Powhatan and his people and exploring more of Chesapeake Bay. Then Newport left for England again and the colonists settled down for another long summer.

By this time everyone recognized John Smith

as the settlement's real leader. It was always he who could handle the Indians and find food when food was scarce. It was always he who thought of a remedy for some desperate situation. Many of the men did not like him, but they could not deny that he had the strength and determination needed to make the colony succeed. For this reason, they elected him President of the governing council.

Another year passed, and another fleet came with new colonists and more supplies. It brought news that a new governor had been appointed. Discouraged and disappointed, Smith decided to go home, but before going he made one last trip to the falls of the James River.

On the way back, a careless companion set fire to the bag of gunpowder which Smith carried around his waist. His clothes caught fire and he would have burned to death had he not jumped into the river.

His men pulled him out and hurried him back to Jamestown, but little could be done for him even there. He was too badly burned to stay. When he was able to be moved, he was carried aboard a ship that was leaving for England. The next day he sailed away, never to return. His Virginia days were over. From now on Jamestown would have to get along without him and his helpful efforts.

On to America

CAPTAIN SMITH sat sunning himself in the bow of the ship "Falcon." The sunshine and fresh air made him feel better than he had felt at any time since his accident, but it was still painful for him to move about. Nevertheless, painful as it was, he had come on deck. If he had to die, he said, he preferred to die looking at the ocean than lying in bed.

Now, relaxed by the wind and the sound of waves slapping against the ship's bow, he began to think. He thought of the last two years in Virginia, wondering why events there had gone as they had, and he began to think and to plan for the future. He had learned much in Jamestown and meant to share his learning with his friends at home.

Suddenly his thoughts were interrupted by the sound of footsteps. The captain of the "Falcon" was approaching.

"Don't bother to stand, Captain," the latter said, sitting beside him. "Are you enjoying the fresh air?"

Smith nodded. "It's wonderful." Then he added with a frown, "But I'd be happier if I could move about and help with the work."

"No one doubts that you will work again as soon as your burns are healed. In fact, the men are hoping you won't get well before we get back to England."

Smith looked puzzled and the captain chuckled. "They don't bear you any ill will, Captain, but they talked with the settlers in Jamestown. They heard how you set an example there by working harder than anyone else in the settlement. They were told you had men whipped and even threatened to banish them from the settlement because they wouldn't work."

Smith straightened himself. "Sir, if I had not made people work you would not have found one Englishman alive in Jamestown."

"I believe you," said the "Falcon's" captain. "Jamestown was very fortunate to have you. Without your courage and ability to work and to get along with the Indians, there would be no Virginia today."

Smith was embarrassed. He was not accustomed to being complimented. The captain's words set him thinking, however. If he ever returned to America, he would not go to Jamestown. Instead, he would explore the coastline farther north, which John and Sebastian Cabot and his friend Bartholomew Gosnold had explored. He would make a map of it which other people could use. That part of the country seemed more promising than Virginia.

By December, 1609, Captain Smith was home in Willoughby. His leg healed slowly, but he could get around a little. He enjoyed sitting before the fireplace where he had spent so many hours as a boy. He enjoyed talking with his friends and telling the children stories.

He was the children's favorite. Several times a day they would gather around him. "Uncle John! Uncle John! Tell us a story." Then they would grow quiet as mice as he told them one of his adventures.

They liked his Indian stories best of all. Their favorite was about the little girl Pocahontas, who had saved his life. Every time he repeated this story, they were afraid he would be killed and were always happy when he told them how Pocahontas saved him.

The following summer Smith received bad

news from Jamestown. Of the five hundred people living there when he had left, only sixty survived the winter. It had been a hard winter, the "starving time," as the settlers called it. John Smith had been missed. There was no one else to make the colonists work, no one brave enough or shrewd enough to make the Indians trade with them. Now perhaps the settlers recognized, as did the Virginia Company in London, that without Smith the colony would have failed completely.

All that was behind him, however. Since he could do little physical work, he finished his map of Virginia and Chesapeake Bay and wrote a book describing the country and its people. These did much to make him famous.

Four years passed before he was able to travel again. By that time, he had already planned his next voyage.

In Virginia he had liked most of all to explore

new country and make maps and to trade with the Indians. This time he wanted to prove that a voyage of exploration could bring back valuable information and make money for its backers as well.

During the winter of 1613 he and several friends obtained two ships. For his crews, he hired men who were interested in adventure and were not afraid of hard work.

At last the eve of departure came. The ships were ready and the crews had come aboard. Feelings were tense among the men. Some wondered whether they should go to a strange land so far from home. Others wondered whether they would ever return to England.

That night Captain Smith gathered his men together. "Men, we sail in the morning before dawn," he said. "If anyone has ideas about not working on this voyage or is afraid to go, let him leave the ships now. We are not going to

America to fight Indians or to establish a colony. We are going on a peaceful voyage to fish and trade for furs."

"When will we get home?" asked one of the younger sailors.

"If we all work hard and work together, we should be home before Christmas."

The men cheered.

The ships left England the first week in March. On the last day of April they sighted the coast of the New World, far north of Virginia and the Jamestown settlement. From Gosnold and others, Smith had heard of the fine fishing there. He had decided to concentrate on catching fish, then trade for furs and explore the coast.

He had brought along the best maps of this part of the coast that he could find. Now he discovered that they were worthless. Immediately he set his men to work measuring distances between islands and headlands and measuring the depth of the water. He made sketches of the shoreline and lengthy notes of everything that he saw. If no good maps were available, then he would make one. Since much of the coast reminded him of England, he decided to call the country New England.

Six months later he and his men were back in England. The trip was a great success and his fame as an explorer and trader spread quickly. But most important of all, perhaps, he had given New England a name and had made it known to his countrymen.

A year later, Smith sailed for New England again. This time he was not so fortunate, for he and his ships were captured by pirates. However, his name was known even among pirates, he discovered. Although he was a prisoner, the captain treated him almost as if he were an honored guest.

186

Smith was amused. He was also surprised by the pirates' poor seamanship and gunnery. "Captain," he said one day, "if you insist on being a pirate, let me teach you to be a good one. You know nothing about fighting."

After that, except when attacking an English ship, Smith stood at the captain's side and gave him advice.

The captain was grateful. "You've been generous," he said one day. "Now it's my turn to be generous with you. Here is money to get you to England. Tonight my men will take the small ship and put you ashore in France."

Smith bowed politely. "Thank you, sir. I shall be glad to go home."

That night, just before reaching shore, the sailors seized Smith and took away the money the captain had given him. "Why should he have it?" they said. "Let's kill him. The captain will never know."

188

Before they could act, however, a storm arose. The boat tossed and tumbled and the pirates went below deck to escape the wind and the driving rain. Smith saw his chance. He crept on deck, untied one of the ship's boats, and let the wind carry him away.

It was all he could do to keep the boat from sinking. He rowed, then bailed, then rowed again. At last he heard the roar of breakers and knew he was close to land. Suddenly the boat leaped up, twisted, spun—and that was all he remembered.

Some time later he was aware of sunlight on his face. "It's a man!" he heard a seemingly distant voice say.

"Is he dead?" asked another voice.

"He must be. Nobody could have lived through that storm last night. Still, we'd better see. Here, help me."

Smith could feel himself being lifted and with

great effort opened his eyes. "I am alive," he said in French. "Please help me."

It was winter before he was able to get to Willoughby. Once again, he found, his brother and sister and their families had given him up for dead.

"You will not have to worry again," he told them. "I'm thirty-six now and it's time for me to stop traveling. From now on I'll spend my time telling people about America. There's fine land there, free for the asking, where Englishmen could make a wonderful life for themselves and their children."

He paused thoughtfully, then added, "It wouldn't be an easy life. They wouldn't find a fortune in gold or precious stones. They would have to work, as all honest men must. But they could build a better world than the one we have here in England. From now on I'm going to work to make that possible."

He wrote books about New England and about ocean travel, in which he sought to encourage people to go to America. He talked with people in high position—government officials, noblemen, wealthy merchants—seeking their support of his plans. He wrote hundreds of letters and, wherever he went, he talked. He praised New England and its opportunities, encouraged the timid, scolded the doubters, advised those who were interested.

Fortunately he lived to see his efforts rewarded. In 1620 Englishmen from his own Lincolnshire sailed with others from the Netherlands to establish the Plymouth colony on Cape Cod. In 1629 still others established the Massachusetts Bay Colony at Boston.

In January of 1631 some of his old friends gathered in Willoughby to help celebrate his fifty-first birthday. His health was poor and his friends knew that he was tired.

"You should take life easy now," one said.

"Yes," said another. "You've done more in your lifetime than three ordinary men."

"Gentlemen," he said, "I *am* taking it easy. However, I have begun to write a history of the sea and I intend to finish it. I intend to work as long as I live."

A few months later, on the first day of summer, June 21, John Smith died while working at his desk. He died with a pen in his hand, not a sword, but he had worked to the end.

Many people paid honor to him as an explorer, colonizer, seaman, and promoter. But it was the common people who, through their bravery and industry in the New World, demonstrated the greatest respect for John Smith and his ideas.

More About This Book

WHEN JOHN SMITH LIVED

1580   JOHN SMITH WAS BORN IN WILLOUGHBY, LIN-COLNSHIRE, ENGLAND.

North America was inhabited only by Indians, except for a few Spanish settlers.

The English were rapidly becoming interested in exploring the New World.

England was ruled by Queen Elizabeth.

1580–   JOHN LIVED WITH HIS PARENTS AND ATTENDED
1596   SCHOOL.

Sir Francis Drake and his men completed their trip around the world, 1580.

First eye-witness drawing of Indians participating in sports made, 1585.

The English established a short-lived colony on Roanoke Island, North Carolina, 1587.

Virginia Dare, first white child born in America, was born on Roanoke Island, 1587.

A rescue expedition found English settlement on Roanoke Island destroyed, 1591.

1596– 1607	SMITH BECAME AN APPRENTICE AND AFTER- WARDS FOUGHT IN EUROPEAN WARS.

Spanish settlers held the first theatrical performance in North America, 1598.

Bartholomew Gosnold, an English explorer, reached the coast of New England, 1602.

France established a short-lived colony in Maine, 1604.

1607– 1609	SMITH HELPED TO ESTABLISH AND GOVERN JAMESTOWN, VIRGINIA.

The first glassmaking in America was undertaken at Jamestown, 1607.

The first cargo was shipped from America to England, 1608.

1609– 1631	SMITH EXPLORED NEW ENGLAND AND WROTE BOOKS ABOUT THE NEW WORLD.

The Dutch founded New Amsterdam, which afterward became New York, 1612.

John Rolfe planted the first successful tobacco crop in Virginia, 1612.

The Plymouth colony in New England was founded in 1620, and Boston, 1630.

1631   JOHN SMITH DIED AT WILLOUGHBY, JUNE 21.

England was ruled by James I.

There were scattered English and Dutch settlements in America.

The estimated population of the colonies was about 7,900.

DO YOU REMEMBER?

1. How was John helping his mother at the beginning of the story?

2. What interesting things did John see when he went to play in the marsh?

3. Why did Lord Willoughby give John a sheepskin after the sheep shearing?

4. What did John see and do when he went to a fishing village with his father?

5. What happened to John and Robert after they found the bee tree in the forest?

6. What code did John and Robert use when they wanted to signal each other?

7. What narrow escape did John and Robert have on their trip to Thieves' Island?

8. How did the Willoughby family celebrate the Christmas holidays?

9. Why was young Smith unhappy when he returned to the farm following his father's death?

10. Who was David Hume and how did he affect Smith's activities and life?

11. How did Smith become a captain in the Hungarian army?

12. Why did Smith become interested in America and decide to come here?

13. How did Smith help to establish and save the English settlement at Jamestown?

14. What did Smith do after he returned to England to live?

IT'S FUN TO LOOK UP THESE THINGS

1. Where is Smith's birthplace, Willoughby, located in England?

2. Why were the marshes in England favorable to the growth of many plants and animals?

3. Where were the Low Countries of Europe and what war was being fought there?

196

4. Why were many wars fought in Europe about the time Smith lived?

5. Why did many persons in England become interested in coming to America?

6. How did the Indians of Virginia live at the time when Jamestown was settled?

INTERESTING THINGS YOU CAN DO

1. Draw a map to show where the settlement of Jamestown was located.

2. Collect illustrations of the Jamestown settlement for an exhibit on the bulletin board.

3. Make a list of important new products which European explorers found in America.

4. Prepare a chart with dates showing important early settlements in North America.

5. Read about Sir Francis Drake's trip around the world and prepare a report.

6. Find out what people explored New England several centuries before Smith.

7. Name other famous English explorers and settlers who came to America.

OTHER BOOKS YOU MAY ENJOY READING

John Smith, Man of Adventure, Miriam E. Mason. Houghton Mifflin.

Life of John Smith, English Soldier, Ronald Syme. Morrow.

Pocahontas: Brave Girl, Flora Warren Seymour. Trade and School Editions, Bobbs-Merrill.

Powhatan and Captain Smith, Olga Hall-Quest. Farrar-Straus.

Virginia Dare: Mystery Girl, Augusta Stevenson. Trade and School Editions, Bobbs-Merrill.

World of Captain John Smith, Genevieve Foster. Scribner.

INTERESTING WORDS IN THIS BOOK

alder (ôl'dẽr) : tree that grows in moist ground near marshes, swamps, or streams

apprentice (ă prĕn'tĭs) : person bound by legal agreement to serve another in return for instruction in a trade or skill

breaker (brāk'ẽr) : wave breaking into foam on a beach or shore

carcass (kär′kas) : body of a dead animal

crane (krān) : bird with long legs and a long neck and bill which lives near water

crow's nest (krōz′ nĕst′) : partly enclosed platform on the mast of a ship, used as a lookout

currant (kûr′ănt) : berry in the gooseberry family, used chiefly for jelly and jam

dawdle (dô′d′l) : linger, waste time

desperation (dĕs′pēr ā′shŭn) : despair or hopelessness, with a degree of recklessness

frumenty (frōō′mĕn tĭ) : stew or pudding made of wheat, currants, raisins, spices, and milk

guardian (gär′dĭ ăn) : person responsible for the care and education of a child

kilt (kĭlt) : short skirt-like garment once worn by Scotchmen

manor house (măn′ēr hous′) : large mansion or house where the owner of an estate lives

mire (mīr) : soft mud or wet spongy earth

misery (mĭz′ēr ĭ) : state of being wretched, as from poverty or ill health

nectar (nĕk′tēr) : sweet liquid secreted by many kinds of flowers

peat (pēt) : soil composed of decayed plant and animal life which may be used as fuel

pike (pīk) : long sharp-toothed fish

poacher (pōch'ēr) : person who catches fish or game illegally

province (prŏv' ĭns) : part of a country

quay (kē) : paved landing place where ships may load or unload cargo

sapling (săp'lĭng) : young tree

stampeding (stăm pēd'ĭng) : running wildly in a frightened state

stench (stĕnch) : disagreeable odor, often caused by decaying plant and animal life

tenant (tĕn'ănt) : person who lives in or on the property of another, either by agreement or through the payment of rent

tendon (tĕn'dŭn) : tough tissue connecting a muscle with another part of the body

tug (tŭg) : part of a harness

tuition (tŭ ĭsh ŭn) : price paid for instruction

tutor (tū'tēr) : private teacher

valet (văl'ĕt) : personal servant

vault (vôlt) : leap over something by means of a long pole

wassail bowl (wŏs' 'l bōl') : bowl filled with ale or wine flavored with spices, sugar, and roasted apples, served on holidays

200

Childhood
OF FAMOUS AMERICANS

COLONIAL DAYS

JAMES OGLETHORPE, *Parks*
JOHN ALDEN, *Burt*
MYLES STANDISH, *Stevenson*
PETER STUYVESANT, *Widdemer*
POCAHONTAS, *Seymour*
PONTIAC, *Peckham*
SQUANTO, *Stevenson*
VIRGINIA DARE, *Stevenson*
WILLIAM BRADFORD, *Smith*
WILLIAM PENN, *Mason*

STRUGGLE for INDEPENDENCE

ANTHONY WAYNE, *Stevenson*
BEN FRANKLIN, *Stevenson*
BETSY ROSS, *Weil*
CRISPUS ATTUCKS, *Millender*
DAN MORGAN, *Bryant*
ETHAN ALLEN, *Winders*
FRANCIS MARION, *Steele*
GEORGE ROGERS CLARK, *Wilkie*
GEORGE WASHINGTON, *Stevenson*
ISRAEL PUTNAM, *Stevenson*
JOHN HANCOCK, *Cleven*
JOHN PAUL JONES, *Snow*
MARTHA WASHINGTON, *Wagoner*
MOLLY PITCHER, *Stevenson*
NATHAN HALE, *Stevenson*
NATHANAEL GREENE, *Peckham*
PATRICK HENRY, *Barton*
PAUL REVERE, *Stevenson*
TOM JEFFERSON, *Monsell*

EARLY NATIONAL GROWTH

ABIGAIL ADAMS, *Wagoner*
ALEC HAMILTON, *Higgins*
ANDY JACKSON, *Stevenson*
DAN WEBSTER, *Smith*
DeWITT CLINTON, *Widdemer*
DOLLY MADISON, *Monsell*
ELI WHITNEY, *Snow*
ELIAS HOWE, *Corcoran*
FRANCIS SCOTT KEY, *Stevenson*
HENRY CLAY, *Monsell*
JAMES FENIMORE COOPER, *Winders*
JAMES MONROE, *Widdemer*
JOHN AUDUBON, *Mason*
JOHN JACOB ASTOR, *Anderson*
JOHN MARSHALL, *Monsell*
JOHN QUINCY ADAMS, *Weil*
LUCRETIA MOTT, *Burnett*
MATTHEW CALBRAITH PERRY, *Scharbach*
NANCY HANKS, *Stevenson*
NOAH WEBSTER, *Higgins*
OLIVER HAZARD PERRY, *Long*
OSCEOLA, *Clark*
RACHEL JACKSON, *Govan*
ROBERT FULTON, *Henry*
SAMUEL MORSE, *Snow*
SEQUOYAH, *Snow*
STEPHEN DECATUR, *Smith*
STEPHEN FOSTER, *Higgins*
WASHINGTON IRVING, *Widdemer*
ZACK TAYLOR, *Wilkie*

WESTWARD MOVEMENT

BRIGHAM YOUNG, *Jordan and Frisbee*
BUFFALO BILL, *Stevenson*
DANIEL BOONE, *Stevenson*
DAVY CROCKETT, *Parks*
GAIL BORDEN, *Paradis*
JED SMITH, *Burt*
JESSIE FREMONT, *Wagoner*
JIM BOWIE, *Winders*
JIM BRIDGER, *Winders*
KIT CARSON, *Stevenson*